Rose /.

► Sarah Bell ◄

The British Columbia
Lodge & Resort
Guide

Also Includes the Banff/Jasper Area and the Yukon

151 Choices, from No-frill Cabins to
Full-facility Resort Hotels

Gordon Soules Book Publishers Ltd.
West Vancouver, Canada
Seattle, USA

Canadian Cataloguing in Publication Data

Bell, Sarah.
The British Columbia lodge and resort guide

Includes index.
ISBN 0-919574-80-7

1. Resorts—British Columbia—Directories.
2. Resorts—Alberta—Directories.   3. Resorts—
Yukon Territory—Directories.   4. British
Columbia—Guidebooks.   5. Alberta—Guidebooks.
6. Yukon Territory—Guidebooks.   I. Title.
TX907.5.C22B753   1993   647.94711'01'025
C93-091551-8

Published in Canada by
Gordon Soules Book Publishers Ltd.
1352-B Marine Drive
West Vancouver, BC
Canada   V7T 1B5

Published in the U.S.A. by
Gordon Soules Book Publishers Ltd.
620 – 1916 Pike Place
Seattle, WA 98101

Cover design by Harry Bardal
Typesetting by A.R. CompuType Graphics, Vancouver, Canada
Printed and bound in Canada by Hignell Printing Limited

Contents

Prices quoted in this book are in Canadian funds.

Information in any guidebook is subject to change or error. We suggest you confirm important details at the time you make reservations.

While great care has been taken to ensure the accuracy of the information in this book, neither the author nor the publisher can accept responsibility for any outdated information, omissions, or errors.

Darlene Marzari

Welcome to British Columbia

Welcome to "Super, Natural British Columbia," known around the world for its spectacular scenery and terrific hospitality.

From the dense, lush forests and rugged terrain of the coast to the dramatic peaks of the Rockies, British Columbia more than lives up to its reputation.

I hope you are able to visit our many beautiful regions, which include a wide diversity of geography, climate, and cultural events.

Just for starters, enjoy whale-watching on Vancouver Island, wildlife viewing in the Peace River country, or panning for gold at Barkerville. Join in the fun skiing or snowmobiling on some of the finest mountains in the world, sample wines of the highest quality in the wineries of the Okanagan, and visit mystical Haida Gwaii (also known as the Queen Charlotte Islands).

Needless to say, fishing is great just about anywhere in British Columbia—whether it's for trophy-sized coho and chinook salmon on the coast, world-famous Kamloops trout in the interior, landlocked Kokanee salmon in the Kootenays, or steelhead in the northwest. For the adventurous, a river rafting trip might add an exciting dimension to a more traditional fishing vacation.

And don't miss the great cities of the province, including Victoria and Vancouver, which offer cultural events for every taste.

As Minister of Tourism and Minister Responsible for Culture, I hope you have a terrific holiday in our beautiful province.

Darlene Marzari
Minister of Tourism
and Minister Responsible for Culture

Province of
British Columbia

Minister of Tourism and
Minister Responsible
for Culture

Parliament Buildings
Victoria, British Columbia
V8V 1X4

Oak Bay Beach Hotel

1175 Beach Drive
Victoria, BC   V8S 2N2
(604) 598-4556
Fax: (604) 598-4556

On the waterfront at Oak Bay in Victoria.

Fifty-one rooms: One or two people, October 16 to March 11 $78–273,
March 12 to June 11 $88–303, June 12 to October 15 $88–383.

A Tudor-style hotel among gardens and lawns, with an ocean beach and a view of Mount Baker and passing boats. Guest rooms have antique furniture and private balconies with a view of the ocean. Some have window seats and four-post beds. Room rates include one high tea or lunch cruise per stay. Complimentary morning tea and coffee are served in a lobby with grand piano, traditional fireplace, and antique furniture. Afternoon high tea is served in a formal dining room. The dining room and a British-style pub have decks with ocean views. Guests take lunch and sunset dinner cruises on the hotel's yacht and salmon fishing and killer whale watching cruises on the M.V. *Pride of Victoria*. Popular Victoria attractions include the Royal British Columbia Museum, the legislative buildings, and the Butchart Gardens. Specialty shops at Oak Bay Village are minutes away.

Victoria Regent Hotel

1234 Wharf Street
Victoria, BC   V8W 3H9
(604) 386-2211
Fax: (604) 386-2622

Located in the heart of downtown Victoria.

Fifty rooms: October to May $95–595, May to June $115–595, July to September $140–695. Honeymoon, golf, and fishing packages available.

A waterfront hotel with private moorage, originally built as a condominium complex. The hotel's Water's Edge Café, which has views of Victoria's inner harbour, is open as a licensed lounge in the evenings. Apartment-style penthouses and suites have sun decks and kitchens. Some also have fireplaces and Jacuzzis. Complimentary services include secured underground parking, daily newspaper, and movie channel. The hotel is within easy walking distance of the Royal London Wax Museum, the Undersea Gardens, the Royal British Columbia Museum, the provincial parliament buildings, and many of Victoria's shops and restaurants.

Arundel Manor Bed and Breakfast

June Earl
980 Arundel Drive
Victoria, BC   V9A 2C3
(604) 385-5442

Five kilometres (3 miles) from city centre—off Admirals Road, between
Highway 1 and Gorge Road (Highway 1A).

Five rooms: Two people $75–95.

A 1912 heritage house that has preserved the fine craftsmanship of its day—original wood panelling, sturdy beams, and a stone fireplace in a spacious guest sitting room. Four of the bedrooms have king- or queen-sized beds and ensuite bathrooms, and two also have large balconies where guests watch the sun setting over the sea. A fifth bedroom has twin beds and a private bathroom. A breakfast with hot entrée is served in a dining room. The half-acre property slopes down to Portage Inlet, a bird sanctuary that is home to blue herons, Canada geese, swans, ducks, and bald eagles. In spring, herons can be seen nesting in Colquitz Park, a short walk away. The Gorge Walkway is also within walking distance. The salmon spawning that takes place every fall in Goldstream Park is a short drive away. Adult oriented. Smoking outdoors only. Not suitable for pets. Reservations essential. Cancellation notice seven days.

Brentwood Bay Bed and Breakfast

Evelyn Hardy
7247 West Saanich Road
Mail: Box 403
Brentwood Bay, BC V0S 1A0
(604) 652-2012

At the corner of Stelly's Cross Road and West Saanich Road, a 20-minute drive east of Victoria.

Thirteen rooms: Two people $69–185, add'l person $15. Includes breakfast.

Two-room housekeeping cottage (sleeps three people): $115. Does not include breakfast.

A rural heritage house built in 1912 that offers various accommodation choices, self-catered or with country breakfast provided. There is a separate, secluded cottage. In the main house, rooms on the lower level share a common area with a kitchenette and a fireplace. One room has been adapted for people using wheelchairs. Most of the upstairs rooms have views of the bay. The attic hideaway has a Jacuzzi. Many rooms feature fireplaces, candlelight, and roses. Boating, fishing, and golf are nearby and Butchart Gardens a five-minute drive away. No pets. No smoking. No credit cards. Family, business, and cycling groups welcome.

Swallow Hill Farm Bed and Breakfast

Gini and Peter Walsh
4910 William Head Road
Mail: RR 1
Victoria, BC V9B 5T7
(604) 474-4042

From Victoria, take Highway 1A west to Highway 14. Follow Highway 14 towards Sooke. Turn south at Metchosin Road, which becomes William Head Road. Watch for sign 2 kilometres (1 mile) past Metchosin Country Store.

Two suites: One person $65, two people $75, add'l person $15.

Off-season rates: One person $55, two people $65. Discount on long stays.

A small working farm among open fields and meadows, with views of the ocean, the Olympic Mountains, and Mount Baker. One suite has its own entrance, deck, queen-sized bed, ensuite, microwave, and wet bar. An upstairs suite has queen-sized and twin beds, private bathroom, and porch. Complimentary tea, coffee, and biscuits are provided in suites. Breakfast includes fresh eggs and juice from home-grown apples. Old-fashioned country picnics and champagne-breakfast weekends are offered. The house has handcrafted furniture and antique Canadi-ana. The farm has chickens, geese, ducks, sheep, a vegetable garden, a large duck pond, and an orchard with twelve varieties of apples from around the world. Nearby amenities include Sooke Harbour House for dining and the Olympic View Golf Club. There are trails, beaches, parks, and wildlife in the area. No pets (dog in residence). No smoking.

Sooke Harbour House

Fredrica and Sinclair Phillips
1528 Whiffen Spit Road
Mail: RR 4
Sooke, BC   V0S 1N0
(604) 642-3421
(604) 642-4944

Located 32 kilometres (23 miles) northwest of Victoria, just outside
Sooke.

Thirteen rooms: One or two people $155–275, add'l person $25. Rates
include breakfast and lunch.

An inn internationally recognized for its cuisine and accommodation, on a bluff overlooking a cove beside the Strait of Juan de Fuca. The view from the resort often includes seals
and otters at play. An extensive kitchen garden provides organic herbs, edible flowers,
and vegetables for meals. Three guest rooms, including a honeymoon suite, are in the
original inn. The other ten are in an adjacent guest house. One room in the guest house
is wheelchair accessible. Each room has an ocean view, a balcony or terrace, antique furniture, a sitting area with fireplace, and a private bathroom. Some have four-post beds,
Jacuzzi tubs for two, skylights, and wet bars stocked with herbal teas, coffee, and cook-
ies. Original art on the walls. Sooke Harbour House has been ranked one of the 10 best
restaurants in Canada by *Where to Eat in Canada*, given four stars by *Best Places* and
four kisses by *Best Places to Kiss in the Northwest*, and described as "one of the prettiest,
most idyllic country inns in North America" by the *Los Angeles Times*.

Ocean Wilderness Country Inn

Captain Bill and Marion Paine
109 West Coast Road
Mail: RR 2
Sooke, BC V0S 1N0
(604) 646-2116
Fax: (604) 646-2116

Forty-eight kilometres (30 miles) from
Victoria on West Coast Road (Highway 14).

Seven rooms: Two people $85–175, add'l
person $15 with cot or $25 with hide-a-bed. Rates include breakfast. Winter rates available November to May.

An inn on five acres of wooded oceanfront, with a view of the Strait of Juan de Fuca and the Olympic Mountains. The original log house serves as dining room and common area for the inn. A new wing contains large guest rooms with Persian carpets, canopied beds, wet bars, and private bathrooms. Room rates include breakfast. A silver service of coffee with a miniature vase of flowers is delivered in the morning to guest-room doors. Dinner by arrangement. A hot tub in a Japanese gazebo is available for a private soak.

Burnside House Bed & Breakfast

Renate and Heinz Tilly
1890 Maple Avenue
Mail: Box 21 RR 4
Sooke, BC V0S 1N0
(604) 642-4403

Just past Sooke; 37 kilometres (23 miles)
west of Victoria.

Four rooms: Two people $70–125, based on
two-night stay; add'l person $15. Off-season
rates available October 15 to May 1, not including weekends or holidays.

A restored Georgian-style country house. Built by John Muir in 1870, Burnside is the oldest inhabited house in Sooke. Rooms have queen-sized or double beds and private bathrooms; some rooms have ocean and mountain views. Breakfast is served in the guests' living room, which has a TV, games, and a fireplace. Vegetarian breakfasts available. Hot tub on the premises. Golfing, swimming, hiking, and trout and salmon fishing are nearby. Guests watch for whales and seals from the beaches. Complimentary bicycles provided. Pets welcome. Non-smokers preferred. Children over 12. Visa and MasterCard. Deposit of one night's rate required to hold reservation; cancellation notice 72 hours. Accessible by public transit. Wir sprechen Deutsch.

Hastings House

Pamela and Hector de Galard
160 Upper Ganges Road
Mail: Box 1110
Ganges, Salt Spring Island, BC   V0S 1E0
(604) 537-2362
Fax: (604) 537-3333

Within walking distance of the village of Ganges, overlooking the
harbour. Accessible by ferry or float plane.

Twelve rooms: One or two people $220–330 in low season, $290–420
in peak season. Includes breakfast and afternoon tea. On weekends,
two-night bookings only. Closed December to mid-March.

A Tudor-style manor house on the ocean with well-kept lawns and gardens. Sheep are
seen cropping the nearby hills. Hastings House's grounds, interior décor, cuisine, and
service have built an international reputation. Spacious guest rooms have antiques and
chintz-draped beds. Each room has chocolates on the bedside table, a fire in the fireplace,
and morning coffee delivered to the door. Afternoon tea is served with silver and crystal.
Cocktails are served before dinner in a sitting room with stone fireplace. Nearby are golfing, sea-kayaking, bird-watching, fishing, and renowned artists' studios. Sunday brunch,
served between 11:00 a.m. and 1:00 p.m. ($18.95 per person), is open to the public—
reservations essential. No pets. Reservations required. Awarded a Relais & Chateaux Yel-
low Shield, a classification defined as "The refined comfort of a superb residence."

Salty Springs Seaside Mineral Bath Resort

1460 North Beach Road
Mail: RR 4
Ganges, Salt Spring Island, BC   V0S 1E0
(604) 537-4111 (information)
Toll-free: 800-665-0039 (reservations)
Fax: (604) 537-2939

Located on the north end of Salt Spring Island.

One-, two-, and three-bedroom chalets: Two people $99–169, add'l
person $20. Weekly and off-season rates available. Minimum stay two
nights; holiday weekends and summer, minimum stay three nights.

A resort with new seaside chalets, each with its own 70-airjet natural mineral bath and
a panoramic ocean view, on 29 forested acres with a secluded beach. Each one-, two-,
or three-bedroom chalet has a wood-burning fireplace, a library, a complete kitchen with
microwave, and a sun deck with hammock and gas barbecue. Quiet atmosphere; no TVs
or telephones. A pay phone is available. Deer, eagles, and seals are often seen. The resort
provides complimentary mountain bikes and boats and a float and buoy to tie boats to.
The Wallace Island marine park is within rowing distance. Other activities include beachcombing, fishing, and clam digging. Nearby are horseback riding, golf, tennis, and galleries
and studios of artists and craftspeople.

Cusheon Lake Resort

Helmut and Rosemary Boehringer
171 Natalie Lane
Mail: RR 2
Ganges, Salt Spring Island, BC   V0S 1E0
(604) 537-9629

Located 4 kilometres (2 miles) off Fulford-Ganges Road; 8 kilometres (5 miles) from Ganges.

Sixteen chalets (14 log chalets and 2 cedar A-frames): One person $89–145, two people $93–145, add'l person $10–15. Minimum stay three nights in summer, between December 20 and January 6, and on holiday weekends.

A family-oriented resort with 16 chalets in a forest setting on the tip of a secluded peninsula. The chalets have kitchens and are electrically heated, and 14 of them also have open fireplaces. Quiet atmosphere; no TVs or telephones. There is a pay phone at the resort. The lake is warm and is good for swimming and trout and bass fishing. The resort provides boats, floating docks, a sandy beach, picnic tables and chairs, a large brick barbecue with four cooking sites, and an outdoor hot tub that overlooks the lake. Supplies are available in Ganges, a village well worth exploring. Salt Spring Island has parks, galleries, and craft shops. Wildlife and birds are seen at the lake and throughout the island. The resort has been highly recommended by *Horizons Magazine*.

Cedar Beach Resort

1136 North End Road
Mail: RR 4   Site 2   A-1
Ganges, Salt Spring Island, BC   V0S 1E0
(604) 537-2205

Salt Spring
Island

Located on the island's main road.

Seventeen cottages: One person $63–82, two
people $69–104, add'l person $13, child
under 12 $10. Crib, highchair, or cot $5.

On St. Mary Lake

A village of cottages on six forested acres on the shore of St. Mary Lake. Each one- or
two-bedroom self-contained cedar cottage has a fireplace, a sun deck, and cable TV. There
is fishing for trophy trout and bass. Boats and tackle available at reasonable hourly, half-
day, or daily rates. The resort has a sandy beach and a heated swimming pool and sauna
(seasonal) and places to play tetherball, horseshoes, badminton, and volleyball. Golf and
tennis are nearby. Accommodation available for people with disabilities. Receptions and
conferences welcome. Visa and MasterCard accepted.

Maple Ridge Cottages

Lauren Sipone and George Puharich
301 Tripp Road
Mail: RR 1   Site 4 BO
Ganges, Salt Spring Island, BC   V0S 1E0
(604) 537-5977

Five kilometres (3 miles) from Ganges on St.
Mary Lake.

Four cottages: Two people $55–75, add'l
person $10–15. Weekly and off-season rates
available.

A small, quiet resort on Salt Spring Island. Four cottages on two acres of sloping lawns
look over St. Mary Lake to Vancouver's North Shore mountains beyond. Each cottage
has one bedroom with a queen-sized bed, a living room with a double sofa bed, a kitchenette, and a sun deck. Canoes, boats, windsurfers, and sailboats are available for guest
use. The lake offers swimming and fishing, and there are golf and tennis nearby.

Spindrift at Welbury Point

Pippa Maloney and Maureen Bendick
Mail: RR 3
Ganges, Salt Spring Island, BC   V0S 1E0
(604) 537-5311

Six kilometres (4 miles) from Ganges.

Six cottages: Two people $75–125, add'l
person $10–20. Weekly rates available. Open
May to October.

Spindrift is on Welbury Point, a six-acre
peninsula of arbutus and fir groves. Six cottages on the cliff's edge have paths that wind
easily down to private white sand beaches. Small coves and grassy niches along the point
provide quiet seclusion with broad ocean views. The cottages overlook the ocean and have
sun decks, pottery and paintings by local artists, wall-to-wall carpeting, fireplaces, electric heat, kitchens, bathrooms with showers, kitchen and bathroom supplies, linen, and
bedding. Quiet atmosphere; no TVs or telephones. No staff intrusions disturb guest privacy.
A telephone is available for use at the main house. Adults only. Cost of firewood extra.

Cliffside Inn on the Sea

Penny Tomlin
4230 Armadale Road
Mail: Box 50
North Pender Island, BC   V0N 2M0
(604) 629-6691

From the ferry, follow the signs to Hope
Bay. At the Hope Bay dock, take Clam Bay
Road a short distance, then follow Armadale
Road.

Four rooms: Two people $120–220.

A secluded inn with its own mile of beach and estate-like grounds. Views over the Gulf
Islands, with Mount Baker in the background. All rooms have queen-sized beds, feather
quilts, and private bathrooms. Two rooms have fireplaces. A two-day weekend package
includes two nights' accommodation, country breakfast each morning, and a four-course,
candlelit, fireside dinner. By arrangement, guests enjoy a private hot tub session on the
cliff-hanger deck. Inquiries about family and personal counselling sessions, therapeutic
massage sessions, and nature cruises are welcome. Winter and mid-week rates available.
Adults only. Pets by arrangement. Smoking outside only. Visa and MasterCard accepted.

Oceanwood Country Inn

Marilyn and Jonathan Chilvers
630 Dinner Bay Road
Mayne Island, BC V0N 2J0
(604) 539-5074
Fax: (604) 539-3002

From the ferry, turn right on Dalton Drive,
then right on Mariner's Way, and then left
on Dinner Bay Road.

Eight rooms: One person $105–195, two
people $110–200. Rates include breakfast and
afternoon tea.

A Tudor-style inn that opened in 1990, with eight guest rooms, all with private bathrooms
and some with fireplaces, whirlpool baths, and decks. A living room, a library, and a
games room are available exclusively for guests, and a separate room for small business
meetings can be booked. On the waterfront terrace is a large hot tub. There is also a sauna.
An intimate 30-seat restaurant, open for dinner seven nights a week, offers a different
prix fixe menu daily. The extensive wine list is exclusively West Coast, featuring the best
from B.C., Washington, Oregon, and California. Room rates include breakfast and afternoon tea. Children over 16 welcome. No pets.

Mayne Inn

Ken and Dale Dafoe
Mail: C–13 Bennett Bay
Mayne Island, BC V0N 2J0
(604) 539-3122
Fax: (604) 539-5119

From the ferry terminal, follow the signs to
Mayne Inn, approximately 8 kilometres (5
miles) down the road, in Bennett Bay.

Eight rooms: Two people $60.

A newly renovated inn on three acres of grass and woodland on the edge of the ocean.
All rooms have queen-sized beds, ensuite bathrooms, and panoramic ocean views. The
wheelchair-accessible main floor includes a licensed dining room, a licensed lounge with
fireplace, and a large oceanfront deck. Breakfast, lunch, and dinner are offered on the
deck, which offers sunrises over the water and views of the ocean and passing boats. There
is a 40-seat meeting room. No children. No pets. No smoking. Visa and MasterCard
accepted.

Blue Vista Resort

John and Val Walters
Arbutus Drive
Mayne Island, BC   V0N 2J0
(604) 539-2463

*On Mayne Island, a short ferry ride from
either Vancouver or Victoria, at the end of
Arbutus Drive, on Bennett Bay.*

Eight self-contained cottages: One or two
people $50–70, add'l person $10. Discount
on stays of three or more nights.

A resort in a parklike setting with an ocean view, close to beaches. One- and two-bedroom
cottages have sun decks and kitchens; some have fireplaces. Barbecues and adult bicycles
are available. Hiking, cycling, boating, fishing, swimming, scuba diving, kayaking, and
clam digging are popular activities. Sights to see include a lighthouse and church built
in the 19th century. Restaurants, taverns, galleries, and handicrafts are nearby. Reservations recommended. Pets welcome.

East Point Resort

Carol Money
Saturna Island, BC   V0N 2Y0
(604) 539-2975
Fax: (604) 539-5924

*Sixteen kilometres (10 miles) from the ferry,
at the southeastern tip of Saturna Island,
next to the lighthouse. Check-in is at the
Moneys' house, next door to the firehall.*

Six cottages: One person $70–80, two people
$76–86, add'l person $6. July and August,
minimum stay one week; off-season, minimum stay two days.

Fully renovated turn-of-the-century cottages on seven parklike waterfront acres with a
gradually sloping sandy beach. The spacious West Coast–style one- and two-bedroom cottages have kitchens, bathrooms, and decks with views. Each cottage has glass across its
entire front, vaulted ceilings, and a cedar feature wall. Fishing and nature walks are popular.
Motorboats can be rented by the day or week. A cement boat ramp is available for guests'
use. The resort provides a base for many sightseeing day trips by ferry. Reservations
required. Pets welcome with doggy scoop.

Breezy Bay Bed and Breakfast

Betty Speers
131 Payne Road
Mail: Box 40
Saturna Island, BC   V0N 2Y0
(604) 539-2937

A short drive or a 20-minute walk from the ferry. From the ferry dock, take East Point Road for 1 kilometre (1 mile). Turn right on Payne Road.

Four rooms: One person $45, two people $60, add'l person $10–15. Reduced rates for longer stays and groups.

A restored farmhouse, surrounded by orchards, pasture with sheep, and woodland, offering a quiet, relaxed atmosphere. Breezy Bay, with its herons, eagles, and otters, is a two-minute walk away. An upstairs library, a living room, and a spacious verandah are shared with the host. By arrangement, guests use the kitchen to prepare meals other than breakfast, join in the host's Saturday barbecue at the badminton court, or have a guided walking tour of the island. Children welcome. No pets because of the farm animals. Smoking outside only.

Bodega Resort

Porlier Pass Drive
Mail: Box 115
Galiano Island, BC   V0N 1P0
(604) 539-2677

From the ferry, follow Porlier Pass Drive north to Cook Road. Bodega Resort is the first entrance on the right.

Seven cottages: One person $60, two people $80, add'l person $15, child $5.
Two B&B rooms in lodge: One person $35, two people $60.

A lodge with two bed and breakfast rooms and secluded, spacious, self-contained log cottages on 50 acres of meadows and trees, with views of the ocean and distant islands. The lodge, constructed mostly of logs, has two rooms for guest accommodation. Rates for the rooms include hot breakfast. The farm has sheep, a stocked trout pond for guests to fish in, and guided trail rides (10 horses, $14 an hour each). Dining facilities for groups only. Facilities for meetings and small conventions of up to 30 people. No pets because of the livestock.

Deer Lodge Motel

Bob and Doris Bieberdorf
2529 Highway 1
Mail: RR 1
Mill Bay, BC   V0R 2P0
(604) 743-2423

From Victoria, drive 40 kilometres (25 miles)
north on Highway 1. Deer Lodge Motel is on
the east side of the highway, just before Mill
Bay.

Twenty-four units and three B&B rooms: One person $45–65; two people, double bed $55–75; two people, twin beds $65–95; two-bedroom unit $95; meeting room $85.

A 1947 lodge on four acres of immaculate lawns and gardens, with views of the ocean and the Gulf Islands. Accommodation choices include lodge rooms, apartment-style suites with separate bedrooms and kitchens in the north wing, studio-style units with kitchenettes in the new south wing, and B&B rooms with private bathrooms in the hosts' quarters in the lodge. The rooms and suites have cable TV, complimentary coffee, balconies, and gas barbecues. Most have wood-burning fireplaces. The lodge has a whirlpool and a sauna. Watching the sun rise over snow-capped Mount Baker is an extra treat. Three rooms are wheelchair accessible.

Rosebank Cottages

Anthony and Naomi Abbott
2631 Mill Bay Road
Mill Bay, BC   V0R 2P0
(604) 743-5541

A 30-minute drive north of Victoria on
Vancouver Island.

Five cottages: Two-bedroom $70 ($470 per week), one-bedroom $60 ($420 per week), add'l person $5 ($10 per week).
Two motel units: $55 ($365 per week), add'l person $5 ($10 per week).
Rates based on double occupancy. October to April 10% discount.

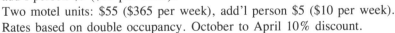

Oceanfront cottages and motel units on landscaped grounds, with views of Mill Bay, Saanich Peninsula, and Mount Baker. Guests play golf at a nearby course or stroll along the beach to rent boats for fishing. No traffic noise disturbs the quiet, yet shopping is an easy walk or cycle away. All cottages and motel units have kitchens. Family oriented, with a sandbox and swing for children and a barbecue pit. Deposit of one night's rate (or $100 for weekly stays) required to hold reservation. Small pets welcome if kept on leashes.

Fairburn Farm Country Manor

Anthea and Darrell Archer
3310 Jackson Road
Mail: RR 7
Duncan, BC V9L 4W4
(604) 746-4637

*Located 11 kilometres (7 miles) southwest of Duncan, approximately 48
kilometres (30 miles) north of Victoria and 48 kilometres (30 miles)
south of Nanaimo.*

Six rooms: Two people $90–125, add'l person $15. Country breakfast
included.
Farm manager's cottage: One to four people $650 per six-day week,
add'l person $10. Single and family rates available. Self-contained.
Open Easter to Halloween.

A 19th-century manor house on a secluded 130-acre sheep farm. Large bedrooms have
queen-sized or twin beds or are family style. Some have ensuite bathrooms, whirlpool
tubs, and fireplaces. Two large porches and two sitting rooms with books and gas fireplaces are for guest use only. Most food served in the large dining room is grown on
this organic farm. The hostess grinds wheat for baking and churns cream into butter for
a farm-fresh breakfast. Other meals by arrangement. Guests go on walks around the farm,
hike into the surrounding forest, help with collecting eggs and milking a cow, and enjoy
other seasonal activities. Listed in Fodor's *Canada's Great Country Inns*. Reservations
required. Smoking outdoors only. No pets; a sheep dog lives with the flock.

Yellow Point Lodge

Mail: RR 3
Ladysmith, BC   V0R 2E0
(604) 245-7422

On Vancouver Island, 34 kilometres (15 miles) south of Nanaimo.

Nine lodge rooms: One person $95–105, two people $153–164.
Beach cabins: One person $105, two people $164.
Beach barracks: One person $54, two people $97.
Add'l person $54. Rates include three meals; mid-morning, afternoon,
and late night tea; and all recreational facilities. October through April,
except weekends and holidays, 20% discount.

A massive log lodge with beach cabins and beach barracks. The lodge's 30-by-60-foot
main lobby has a vast fireplace, big sofas, and a sprung dance floor. Meals are served
at shared tables. The original lodge was built in 1937. When it burned down in 1985,
a team of guest volunteers helped rebuild an almost exact replica. Various rustic cottages
scattered along the beach and among the trees provide privacy and, in many cases, views
of the water. The barracks and some of the cabins have no running water and share camp-
style washrooms. The 180-acre property has a large tract of forest, wildflower meadows,
beaver swamps, and a mile and a half of waterfront with secluded coves and beaches.
The resort offers a sauna and hot tub set among trees, a 200-foot saltwater pool, canoes,
rowboats, mountain bikes, wind surfers, walking and jogging trails, and courts for tennis,
volleyball, and badminton. Killer whales, sea lions, bald eagles, beavers, otters, and minks
are seen. Guests over 16 only. No pets. Deposit of $25 per person required to hold reser-
vation.

Page's Resort and Marina

Ted and Phyllis Reeve
3350 Coast Road, on Silva Bay
Mail: RR 2 Site 30 C–1
Gabriola Island, BC V0R 1X0
(604) 247-8931

Take the hourly ferry from Nanaimo to Gabriola Island. Drive for 20
minutes along either North Road or South Road. Turn onto Coast Road,
and follow it to the sea. Or sail or fly into Silva Bay and tie up at the
dock.

Three cottages: Two people $55–65, add'l person or pet $5.50. Weekly
rates available.
Ten campsites: Two people $10, add'l person $2.50.
Moorage available.

An island retreat that has been welcoming visitors for 50 years. Each cottage has a kitchen
and eating area, a sitting area with hide-a-bed sofa, a bedroom, and a bathroom. Electric
and/or woodstove heating. Dishes, bedding, and firewood are provided. The resort has
a picnic ground, a place to play boules, a marina, art exhibitions, chamber music con-
certs, and a bookstall that features island authors and topics. Guides for hikers and bird-
watchers are available. Guests fish and scuba dive at the resort and swim at nearby Drum-
beg Provincial Park. Reservations essential. Visa and MasterCard accepted. Deposit of
one night's rate to hold reservation; cancellation notice 14 days. Children welcome.

Surf Lodge

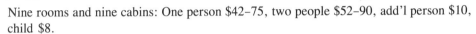

885 Berry Point Road
Mail: RR 1 Site 1 C-17
Gabriola Island, BC V0R 1X0
(604) 247-9231
Toll-free from B.C. and Alberta:
800-361-SURF (7873)
Fax: (604) 247-8336

Located on Gabriola Island, 20 minutes by
ferry from Nanaimo.

Nine rooms and nine cabins: One person $42–75, two people $52–90, add'l person $10, child $8.

A lodge on 10 wooded acres on the shore of Gabriola Island, with sunset views from the dining room, deck, and licensed lounge. All rooms and cabins have ocean views and private bathrooms. The cabins are suitable for families; some have kitchenettes. A living room area in the lodge has books and a stone fireplace. There is a seawater pool. Gabriola offers golf, tennis courts, fishing charters, scuba diving, shoreline and forest walks, several beaches, and petroglyphs.

Eagleshore

893 Shorewood Drive
San Pareil, Parksville, BC V9P 1S6
(604) 248-9311
Fax: (604) 248-5351

One kilometre (1 mile) off the Island
Highway in San Pareil, near Parksville.

One room: One person $65, two people $75.

A bed and breakfast that offers one guest room with French doors opening onto a big private deck, with a walk-on ocean beach for swimming and a view of mountains and islands. The guest room has a queen-sized bed, cable TV, and a large ensuite bathroom. Continental or Canadian breakfast is served. A small art gallery adjoins the dining room. Eagleshore is within strolling distance of pathways through century-old forest and close to a nature preserve and wildlife sanctuary. Animals, songbirds, and bald eagles abound. Nearby are fine restaurants, shopping, golf courses, salmon fishing, and horseback riding. Charters, tee times, and dining reservations can be arranged. Cash and traveller's cheques only. No pets.

Rathtrevor Resort

1035 East Island Highway
Parksville, BC V9P 2E3
(604) 248-2622
Toll-free: 800-661-5494
Fax: (604) 248-0476

One kilometre (1 mile) south of Parksville.

One-, two-, and three-bedroom condominiums: Two people $70–140.
Weekly rates available.

A resort with furnished condominiums in secluded forest settings. Each condominium has a kitchen, a bathroom, a washer and dryer, cable TV, a fireplace, a vaulted ceiling, and a skylight. Bedrooms have queen-sized or twin beds. The condominiums on the bluff have partial ocean views. The resort has a water slide and two outdoor pools (seasonal), a large outdoor hot tub (year-round), a children's playground, a tennis court, a basketball hoop, and volleyball nets. A video arcade games room and a convenience store are open seasonally. VCRs, movies, Nintendo and other games, barbecues, cots, and playpens are available for rent. There is a conference room for meetings and social gatherings. Nearby activities include golfing, fishing, bird-watching, and hiking. Sandy beaches are a few minutes' walk away. Thrill-seeking guests try windsurfing, helicopter touring, or bungee jumping on the Nanaimo River. Shopping, restaurants, gas stations, tourist bureaus, and banks are within five minutes' drive. No smoking. No pets. Minimum stay of three nights between mid-June and mid-September.

Island Hall Beach Resort

Mail: Box 340
Parksville, BC   V9P 2G5
(604) 248-3225
Fax: (604) 248-3125

Located on the beach at Parksville on Vancouver Island.

One hundred rooms: One or two people, January 1 to May 31,
September 16 to December 31, $68–98; June 1 to September 15, $78–
109; add'l person $12; children under 14 free.

A resort on a thousand feet of white sand beach with wide ocean views. There is a good swimming beach, and children's programs are offered during the summer. Rooms are in seven beachfront annexes surrounded by lawns, flowers, and trees. Twenty-eight rooms have kitchenettes. The resort has a restaurant with a view of the ocean, an on-site neighbourhood pub, a central sitting area with armchairs in front of a stone fireplace, volleyball courts on the beach, outdoor tennis courts, croquet, an indoor pool, a whirlpool, a sauna, and a gym. The area offers golfing, scuba diving, deep sea and freshwater fishing, shopping, and, in winter, skiing. The resort, which first opened in 1917, has been modernized and offers convention facilities that include five meeting rooms equipped for up to 225 people.

Grauer's Getaway Destination B&B

Brenda and Steven Grauer
395 Burnham Road
Qualicum Beach, BC   V9K 1G5
(604) 752-5851
Fax: (604) 752-5860

Heading north on Island Highway (19), turn sharply left at Burnham Road (opposite the golf course). Double back up the road. Last house on the left, behind the big cedar hedge.

Two rooms: $85 and up. Discounts on longer or off-season stays.

A traditional house on one acre overlooking Georgia Strait and its islands, with a private pathway to the beach below. Non-smoking rooms are private from the rest of the house. One has twin beds and is furnished with art and antiques; the other has a queen-sized bed and a view of the ocean. Both have private sitting areas and bathrooms. A Continental breakfast of fresh fruit and home-baked items is served in a room overlooking the ocean. On site are a tennis court and ball machine, a pool, a hot tub, private patios for picnics, rose gardens, and an enclosed children's garden. A golf course is a five-minute walk away. The hosts are happy to share their knowledge of the area's many year-round attractions, fine shops, and excellent restaurants. The two rooms make a suite suitable for families. "Grauer's is a unique and beautiful tennis destination," writes Diana Marr in her travel column in *Match Point* magazine. No pets.

Haggard's Cove Resort

Barkley Sound
Mail: Box 396
Port Alberni, BC   V9Y 7M9
(604) 723-8457
Marine Radio: N119983 on Bamfield 27 (Our Way)

Accessible by the M.V. Lady Rose, *a daily passenger ferry from Port Alberni, by float plane, or by boat.*

Four-day/three-night package: $930 per person in party of two, $825 per person in party of three, $750 per person in party of four. Other packages available.

A salmon fishing lodge at the entrance to the Alberni Canal. The boats go out twice a day—from 6:00 a.m. to 9:00 a.m. and again from 4:30 p.m. to 10:30 p.m. The fishing grounds are minutes away in sheltered waters. Guests fish for three types of salmon (chinook, coho, and sockeye) and bottom fish. Each of the five bedrooms has two single beds. Washrooms are shared. Meals are served in the guest sitting/dining room; fresh local seafood is a specialty. Meals, tackle, bait, and a 24-foot cabin cruiser with guide are included in the package rates. Deposit of 25 percent to hold reservation; balance due 60 days before arrival.

Canadian King Lodge

Tzartus Island, Barkley Sound
Mail: 1407 Government Street
Victoria, BC V8W 1Z1
(604) 388-6515

Accessible only by boat or plane. The lodge arranges seaplane flights
from Vancouver and Seattle. The M.V. Lady Rose *calls daily,*
year-round.

Fifteen rooms: $135 per person, meals included.
Off-season rates, group rates, and packages available.

A lodge on a private island in Barkley Sound on the edge of Pacific Rim National Park. The lodge, built of time-weathered stones and massive timbers, has views of the ocean. There is accommodation for up to 24 guests. Each spacious suite has a private bathroom and a deck. On the ground floor, a common area includes a large, open dining room, a rustic lounge, a large living room with fireplace, and a library. Kayaking on an untamed coastline, wildlife photography, West Coast cuisine, isolated coves and beaches, walking in old-growth rainforests, and fishing in a renowned salmon niche in 20-foot Tzar boats with the lodge's experienced guides.

Tyee Resort Conference Centre

Elizabeth and Michael Hicks
Barkley Sound
Mail: Box 32
Bamfield, BC V0R 1B0
(604) 728-3296

On the west coast of Vancouver Island, overlooking Barkley Sound.
Accessible by road, by air from Vancouver or Seattle, or by the M.V.
Lady Rose *from Port Alberni.*

Six rooms and two cottages: Rates vary according to services required.

A resort on four acres of waterfront on one of Canada's finest accessible salmon fishing grounds. The resort specializes in conferences and in corporate fishing trips for groups of 12 in guided 26-foot boats. In the lodge, six spacious guest rooms have views and individual bathrooms; guests share a living room, a bar, and a dining room. A hot tub on the front deck overlooks fishing grounds and islands. Sunset views. Two self-contained waterfront cottages have fireplaces and decks. A five-minute walk away is the fishing village of Bamfield, known for its beaches, trails, and boardwalks.

McKay Bay Lodge

Brian and Cheryl McKay
Mail: Box 116
Bamfield, BC V0R 1B0
(604) 728-3323
(604) 728-3255

Bamfield is on the west coast of Vancouver Island. Accessible by car, by float plane from Port Alberni or Vancouver, or by the M.V. Lady Rose, a coastal freighter, from Port Alberni.

Fishing package: $300 per day.
Boat owners' package: $110 per day.
Nature lovers' package: $95 per day.
Corporate, large group, and low-season rates available.

A lodge on the waterfront in west Bamfield. Each of the seven bedrooms has one double and one single bed and a private ensuite. Common areas include two dining rooms, a large sitting room with fireplace, and a sitting room/games room with bar. An outdoor hot tub overlooks the harbour. A fishing package includes meals, eight to ten hours of guided fishing in roomy boats, gear and tackle, and packaging and fast freezing of the catch. Meals, moorage, and freezing facilities are offered to guests who bring their own boats. A nature lovers' package includes meals, a harbour tour, and an introduction to hiking in the area. Diving and whale-watching expeditions can be arranged.

Bed and Breakfast at Burley's

Ron Burley and Micheline Riley
1078 Helen Road
Mail: Box 550
Ucluelet, BC V0R 3A0
(604) 726-4444

Follow Peninsula Road through Ucluelet, turn left on Marine Drive, right on Helen Road.

Six rooms: One person $35–40, two people $40–50, add'l person $15.

A waterfront home/lodge on a small drive-to island at Ucluelet harbour mouth. Each room has a double bed, twin beds, or a queen-sized bed (water or regular). All rooms have TV. There are views from every window, decks, a large living room, a fireplace, books, and a recreation room with a pool table. Guests hike and pitch horseshoes on the grounds, watch the activities of a lively fishing and logging town, visit the lighthouse and the wharves, fish the open ocean, and watch the whales. No children. No pets. No smoking. Check in by 10:00 p.m., out by 11:00 a.m. Français aussi.

Ocean Village Beach Resort

Alan and Sandra Woodhouse, Bob and Edie Ford
Mail: Box 490
Tofino, BC   V0R 2Z0
(604) 725-3755

Three kilometres (2 miles) south of Tofino.

Fifty-one cottages: One or two people $52–120, add'l person $10, child over five $4. Crib $2 per night or $5 per stay.
Winter discount November 1 to March 11, except over Christmas, on stays of three or more days.

A resort with Gothic-arched cedar cottages that have views of the open ocean. The cottages are either single-storied units, with one or two bedrooms, or two-storied duplexes. Each sleeps four comfortably and has a kitchen and a bathroom with tub/shower combination. The single cottages are set about 25 feet from the high tide line. The duplex cottages are set either about 60 feet or about 160 feet from the high tide line. Quiet atmosphere; no TVs, telephones, or radios in the cottages. There is wheelchair access to the two-bedroom cottages and the beach. The resort has an indoor swimming pool, a hot tub with Jacuzzi, a coin laundry, barbecues, and a horseshoe pit. A small meeting room is available for business conferences and family reunions. Downtown Tofino and its whale-watching vessels, tour boats, charter boats, and fishing guides are a four-minute drive away. Local restaurants feature fresh Dungeness crab and other seafood. Pacific Rim National Park, a nine-hole golf course, an airstrip, and Long Beach are nearby. Guests enjoy beachcombing and seeing the abundant wildlife and birds of the area's beaches and other walking areas. The ocean, often dramatic in winter months, makes the resort popular year-round. Deposit of one night's rate required to hold reservation. Cancellation notice seven days.

Vargas Island Inn

Neil and Marilyn Buckle
Vargas Island
Mail: Box 267
Tofino, BC V0R 2Z0
(604) 725-3309

Three nautical miles (20 minutes by boat) northwest of Tofino on Vargas Island. Boat pick-up at Crab Dock at the foot of Olson Road, Tofino. Call to make arrangements.

Six rooms: One person $60, two people $90, add'l person $10. Rates include boat transportation.

A beachfront wilderness resort in the heart of Clayoquot Sound, facing Meares Island and the mountains of Strathcona Park. The inn marks the east end of a life-saving trail for survivors of shipwrecks, which crosses the island to the open-ocean beaches. Guests row, canoe, fish, whale watch, hike, and fire their own oceanside saunas. The inn has large sitting and dining areas with fireplaces. Bathrooms are shared. Staples, linen, and bedding are provided. Guests supply their own food, which they prepare in the inn's cooking areas. By arrangement, the hosts provide meals, accommodate pets, and arrange day trips. Children over four. Not wheelchair accessible.

Middle Beach Lodge

Jeremy and Veronica Evans
Mail: Box 413
Tofino, BC V0R 2Z0
(604) 725-2900
Fax: (604) 725 2901

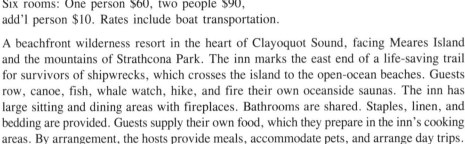

Located 3 kilometres (2 miles) south of Tofino, minutes away from Long Beach and Pacific Rim National Park.

Twenty-four rooms: One or two people $75–100.

Two rooms with bunk beds (each room accommodates four people): One person $25. Rates include breakfast. Closed January and February.

A lodge in a private setting on a warm sandy bay on the open Pacific, with ocean views and sunsets. Two guest rooms have bunk beds; the rest have queen-sized beds. All have private bathrooms. A Continental breakfast is served in a sitting room with a large stone fireplace and a view of the ocean. The lodge has a sun deck, a TV room, and a laundry. Guests walk the lodge's own trails to Templar and McKenzie beaches. Fishing, hiking, golf, surfing, whale watching, and village shopping are all minutes away. Visa and Master-Card. Deposit of two nights' rate required to hold reservation. Cancellation notice seven days. Small pets allowed by special arrangement only.

Sea Breeze Lodge

The Bishops
Hornby Island, BC   V0R 1Z0
(604) 335-2321

From Vancouver Island, take a ferry from
Buckley Bay (just south of Courtenay) to
Denman Island and on to Hornby Island. The
lodge is 11 kilometres (7 miles) from the
Hornby ferry landing.

Twelve cottages: $90 per person per day or
$580 per person per week, meals included. Off-season rates: Two people $58–72, meals
not included. Children's rates available.

A family-oriented lodge on the sandy shores of Tribune Bay. The cottages are self-contained,
have fireplaces, and share a hot tub with an ocean view. Lunches on the patio and smor-
gasborg dinners are included in the summer rates. The lodge has its own grass tennis court.
Nearby Helliwell Park is known for its spring wildflowers. Popular on Hornby Island
are swimming, salmon fishing, hiking, and bird-watching. Pets welcome. Pay phone, camping, and RV parking. Early reservations recommended.

Good Morning Bed 'n' Breakfast

Marian Sieg
7845 Central Road
Hornby Island, BC   V0R 1Z0
(604) 335-1094

On the corner of Central and Sandpiper.

Three rooms: One person $45, two people
$65. In winter, one person $40, two people
$55.

A B&B on Hornby Island, with spacious bedrooms and a guest living room with fireplace, radio, TV, and VCR. Private entrance for guests. Breakfast, consisting of homemade bread, muffins, jams, and a choice of pancakes or free-range eggs and bacon, is
served in the owner's dining room. Guests visit Helliwell Park and its eagles' nesting
grounds or look for fossils on Fossil Beach. Other attractions on Hornby include swimming at three sandy beaches, boating, and hiking the many trails. Kayaks, bikes, and charter
boats for fishing are available. No pets. Smoking on the patio only. Bike storage available.

Killarney Resort

Joy and Art Johnston
8914 Clarkson Drive
Saratoga Beach
Black Creek, BC   V0R 1C0
(604) 337-5459

*One kilometre (1 mile) off Highway 19,
halfway between Courtenay and Campbell
River.*

Seven cottages: Two people $55–75, add'l
person $7. Open May to September.

A resort with seven cottages on two acres of quiet, wooded grounds with a sandy ocean beach. The one- and two-bedroom cottages are equipped for light housekeeping. Guests beachcomb, explore nearby nature trails, hike, rent boats for fishing, golf at the local course, and relax in the sun or shade on the grounds. A library in the hosts' house includes reference books on the local flora and fauna and a selection of games; the hosts enjoy sharing their knowledge of local amenities and animal life. No pets; two cats live here. Advance booking recommended.

Silver King Lodge

Ralph Krentz and Gaye Enns
Mail: Box 351
Campbell River, BC   V9W 5B6
(604) 286-0142

*Just north of Campbell River, on the
northeastern coast of Vancouver Island.*

Rooms: $80 per room.
Fishing packages: Three days/two nights
$1,095, four days/three nights $1,395, four
days/five nights $1,695.

A lodge on the shore of the Inside Passage to Alaska. Fishing packages include professional guides, fishing in 15- and 17-foot Boston Whalers (Tyee-class rowboats also available), fishing tackle, licences, bait, and freezing and packaging of the catch. Smoking and canning also available. A barbecue lunch on shore features fresh salmon, lingcod, and oysters. All other meals, with complimentary drinks, are prepared at the lodge. There are three accommodation areas: the lodge's eight-bedroom upper floor and four-bedroom main floor and a four-bedroom executive cabin. Each is suitable for groups of business associates or friends and has its own entertainment area, bar, and dining facilities. There is full maid service. Hot tub on the deck.

Painter's Lodge

1625 McDonald Road
Campbell River, BC
Mail: Oak Bay Marine Group
1327 Beach Drive
Victoria, BC   V8S 2N4
Toll-free: 800-663-7090
Fax: (604) 598-1361

Five kilometres (3 miles) north of Campbell River. Accessible by road or air. Complimentary shuttle service from Campbell River Airport and downtown Campbell River.

Ninety rooms and four cabins: Call for rates. Fly-in and drive-in fishing packages available. Open April to October.

An oceanfront resort at Campbell River, known as the salmon capital of the world. Originally opened in 1920, Painter's Lodge has long been a salmon fishing hideaway for international celebrities. The resort was completely rebuilt in 1988 and now offers accommodation in a main lodge, five surrounding buildings, and four cabins. Each room has a view of ocean or garden, double or twin beds, a bathroom, and a TV. For fishing guests, the resort has 50 17-foot Boston Whalers with 65 H.P. motors and a centre equipped to freeze, pack, smoke, can, and ship guests' catch. Each boat accommodates two guests and one professional guide. Fishing packages include accommodation, four hours of guided salmon fishing per day, bait, tackle, rain gear, and cleaning and packaging of guests' catch. A fly-in fishing package includes return air fare from Vancouver. A dining room, a licenced lounge with fireplace, a pub, and large patios have panoramic ocean views. The resort has a fitness centre, a massage room, a gift shop, a reading room, a children's games room, bicycle and car rentals, a banquet room for seminars and other gatherings, and a conference centre with banquet facilities, audio-visual equipment, dance floor, bar, and patio with ocean view. On the grounds are tennis courts, a jogging path, a heated pool, hot tubs, and a large barbecue area. Two golf courses are a short drive away.

April Point Lodge

Quadra Island
Mail: Box 1
Campbell River, BC   V9W 4Z9
(604) 285-2222
Fax: (604) 285-2411

Quadra Island is approximately 160 kilometres (100 miles) north of
Vancouver. It can be reached by car ferry from Campbell River on
Vancouver Island or by scheduled floatplane service direct to April
Point.

Forty units: Two people $139–395, add'l person $50, children under 16
free. Fishing and other packages available. Call for rates.

A lodge close to some of B.C.'s finest sport fishing. Professional guides and a fleet of
Boston Whalers equipped with tackle, fuel, rain gear, and bait are available. Staff clean,
freeze, and package the catch. Guests stay in lodge rooms with views of the ocean, rustic
cabins, and deluxe one- to six-bedroom guest houses. West Coast art is featured throughout. Many units have fireplaces, hot tubs, sun decks, and kitchenettes. Waterside meeting
rooms for corporate bookings. The lodge dining room, overlooking Discovery Passage,
specializes in regional cuisine—fresh seafood and meat and locally grown vegetables and
herbs. Extensive quality wine list. Beach picnics, barbecue nights, and traditional native
cooking, including salmon roasted on cedar stakes, bentwood box cooking, and pit cooking. On-site facilities include a fitness room, a gift shop, and a deep water moorage at
a full-service marina. The lodge arranges helicopter-fishing, kayaking, and boat and island
tours. Nearby are two tennis courts, two golf courses, and horseback riding. Eagles, sea
lions, seals, and killer whales are often seen. Deposit of $200 per person required to hold
reservation. Cancellation notice 30 days. Fishing and other packages available.

Discovery House   1-800-668-8054

The Jacobsens
Mail: Box 48
Quathiaski Cove, Quadra Island, BC   V0P 1N0
(604) 285-3146
Fax: (604) 285-3034

Quadra Island is 10 minutes by ferry from Campbell River.

Two beach houses: One or two people $140–180, add'l person $20.
All-inclusive fishing packages: Two people, three days/two nights $729
each, four days/three nights $1,039 each; four people, three days/two
nights $519 each, four days/three nights $759 each. Longer stays by
arrangement.

Private waterfront beach houses with views of Discovery Passage and the coastal mountains. Eagles are often seen in the area, and golfing, hiking, beachcombing, diving, and
horseback riding are nearby. One house has two bedrooms (one is wheelchair accessible)
and two bathrooms (one with a wheelchair shower). Another house has one bedroom and
one bathroom. Both have kitchens, antique furniture, fireplaces, decks, and barbecues.
A hot tub and a heated pool are available for guests' use. The hosts cater meals and prepare food for special diets on request. Fishing packages, which offer fishing for salmon
on light tackle, include everything from pick-up in Campbell River to a 24-foot boat, a
guide, tackle, bait, floater coats, and freezing/packaging of the catch.

Quadra Resort

Joan and John Sell
680 Raydon Road
Mail: Box 638
Quathiaski Cove, Quadra Island, BC V0P 1N0
(604) 285-3279

Located 4 kilometres (2 miles) north of the ferry terminal.

Six guest houses: One or two people $66, add'l person $10. Weekly
rates available. Minimum stay three days.

A resort on the waterfront in Gowlland Harbour. Self-contained guest houses have views
of the harbour. Outside the patio doors are picnic tables where guests sit and watch for
deer, eagles, blue herons, seals, minks, and otters. Canoes are rented on site for exploring the small islands in the harbour. Other boats are rented in Campbell River and moored
at the resort's dock. Experienced fishing guides are available, as are fish-cleaning and
freezing facilities. A cannery and smokehouse are nearby. Guests enjoy wilderness horseback riding, scuba diving, clam digging, photography, and hiking. Sights to see include
the Kwagiulth Museum, petroglyphs, and Rebecca Spit Park. No pets. Cancellation notice
thirty days.

The Brass Bed and Breakfast

Ann Graham
1796 Hyacinthe Bay Road
Mail: Box 299
Heriot Bay, Quadra Island, BC   V0P 1H0
(604) 285-2325
Fax: 285-2305

A 15-minute ferry ride from Campbell River.
Once on Quadra Island, follow the signs to
the Heriot Bay ferry. Watch for the
Hyacinthe Bay Road turnoff on the left.

Three rooms: Two people, double bed $50–60; two people, twin beds $50.
From July 1 to September 1, the house (all three bedrooms) is available by the week only:
$1,000 per week; $200 damage deposit required with reservation.

An oceanfront house on a private beach. The hosts, who live a few minutes' walk away, provide ingredients in the guests' kitchen for guests to make their own breakfast. The house has a living room with large fireplace and country antiques. On the grounds are an orchard, a pond, and a creek. Guests canoe, swim, hike, and use picnic tables and a fire pit on the beach. A Jacuzzi is available. No smoking. No pets (wildlife in the area).

Picard's By the Sea

Bevann and Fred Picard
Mail: Box 165
Mansons Landing, Cortes Island, BC
V0P 1K0
(604) 935-6683

From the Cortes ferry terminal, drive
towards Mansons Landing for approximately
8 kilometres (5 miles). Turn right at Thunder
Road and drive about 90 metres (100 yards).
Also accessible by float plane (private dock).

Two guest rooms: Two people $75, add'l person $20.
Two-bedroom log cabin: $115.
Weekly rates available.

A new, Spanish-style villa on a wooded peninsula in Gorge Harbour, surrounded by water on three sides. Each guest room has a view of the ocean, a patio, a queen-sized bed, a bathroom, and a private entrance. A self-contained two-bedroom log cabin with a view of the ocean has two double beds and a hide-a-bed. There is a games room. Guests go for walks on the grounds and bring their own boats, kayaks, and bicycles to explore the island and Desolation Sound. No smoking or pets. Visa and MasterCard accepted.

Echo Bay Resort

Bob and Nancy Richter
Simoom Sound P.O.
Echo Bay, BC   V0P 1S0
(604) 949-4911

*On the north side of Gilford Island, 45 kilometres (28 miles) northeast
of Port McNeill (north end of Vancouver Island). Accessible by boat or
float plane only.*

Four housekeeping units, each of which sleeps four: $100.
Two penthouse units, each of which sleeps four: $130.
Four-bedroom lodge that sleeps 12: $25 per person; six people
minimum.

An island resort built in 1932 that offers housekeeping units, penthouse units, and a four-bedroom lodge. Each housekeeping or penthouse unit has a bathroom, a bedroom, a kitchenette, and a dining/sitting area and is equipped with cutlery, dishes, cooking utensils, bedding, and towels. Sleeping accommodation is one double bed, one three-quarter bed, a hide-a-bed, and a rollaway. In the lodge, the bedrooms and two bathrooms are upstairs, and a large kitchen and living area are downstairs. A store on site sells groceries and fishing tackle. With advance notice, groups of four or more book full meals for $40 per person per day or dinner only for $25. Moorage is available for boats. The resort rents 14-foot boats with 20 H.P. outboards. The protected waters around the many nearby islands are suitable for day cruising. The second largest marine park in B.C. was recently established in the area. Halibut, salmon, cod, rockfish, prawns, and crabs are abundant. Freezers, smoker, vacuum-packing machine, and crab cooker are available at the resort.

Rivers Lodge

Pat and George Ardley
Dawsons Landing
Rivers Inlet, BC V0N 1M0
(604) 685-2127

Located on the north shore of Walbran Island, 420 air kilometres (260 air miles) from Vancouver. Access by float plane only.

Twelve rooms, two people per room: Four days/three nights $1,795 per person, five days/four nights $2,195, eight days/seven nights $3,295. Rates include return airfare from Vancouver, use of boats with fuel and tackle, rain gear, meals, and snacks.
Arts workshops available.

A lodge in a sheltered cove surrounded by unspoiled wilderness—old-growth forests, wild shorelines, and isolated white sand beaches. The lodge offers ensuite guest rooms, gourmet meals, crab feasts, a saltwater spa, and lounging, dining, and meeting areas. Since opening in 1976, the lodge has earned international renown as a fishing resort. Guests are supplied with two-person, 14-foot fibreglass boats complete with 30 H.P. outboards and tackle. In the varied fish population, chinook salmon predominate. Catches of 30- to 50-pound fish are common. The chef freezes or smokes the guests' catch. In June, early July, and September, arts workshops provide a chance to work with renowned artists in an inspiring setting. A 1,200-square-foot mobile deck becomes a floating classroom, allowing artists to work at sites that do not have shore access. Rates vary depending on the workshop—$1,295 for a four-day workshop, $1,695 for six days. Call for details. Deposit of $500 per person required to hold reservation; balance due 60 days before arrival.

Kenya Court Guest House

Dr. and Mrs. D. Williams
2230 Cornwall Avenue
Vancouver, BC   V6K 1B5
(604) 738-7085

Across from Kitsilano Beach.

Four suites: Two people $85–110, add'l person $40.

A heritage building in one of the most scenic locations in Vancouver, 10 minutes by direct bus line from downtown. Across the street are a popular sandy swimming beach, a large outdoor heated saltwater swimming pool, tennis courts, and seaside paths leading to Granville Island and the Planetarium. Jericho Beach, the University of British Columbia, and the boutiques of Fourth Avenue are close by. Spacious suites have ocean, city, and mountain views. Each suite has a private entrance, one or two bedrooms, private bathroom, TV, telephone, kitchen for snacks, and fireplace. King-sized, queen-sized, and twin beds are available. Breakfast is served in a roof-top solarium with panoramic views. No smoking.

The Country Guest House B&B

Tillie Enns
2829 – 53rd Street (end of Arthur Drive)
Delta, BC   V4K 3N2
(604) 946-9248
Fax: (604) 946-2975

From the Tsawwassen ferry terminal, take Highway 17. Turn west onto 28th Avenue and continue to 53rd Street.

Two rooms in a guest house: One person $65–70, two people $85–95, add'l person $10.

A 10-acre property with trees and horses, close to the Tsawwassen ferry terminal and an hour's drive from the centre of Vancouver. A detached guest house, suitable for families, has two bedrooms, a kitchen, a bathroom, and a living room with stereo, TV, and VCR. Guests have a private patio. A large pool and Jacuzzi are shared with the owner. Ingredients for a Continental breakfast—fruits in season, muffins, preserves, and juice— are supplied in the guest house. No pets. No smoking.

Westwind Tugboat Adventures

Captain Bob Jordan
1160 Holdom Avenue
Burnaby, BC   V5B 3V6
(604) 270-3269
Fax: (604) 270-4245

Phone or fax for a schedule of the tugboats' departure points.

Two restored tugboats: $2,500 per person per week.

Two mobile resorts that take guests along the world-famous Inside Passage between Vancouver, B.C., and Ketchikan, Alaska. The two classic tugboats, *Parry* and *Union Jack*, have been meticulously restored to house 8 to 12 guests in large two-berth cabins. The tugs visit remote areas that cruise ships cannot reach. Tackle and 14-foot skiffs are provided for fishing and exploring the intricate coastline. Clam digging and crabbing, barbecuing fresh seafood on the beach, swimming in warm-water lakes, and visiting hot springs, abandoned canneries, and ghost towns. Options include scheduled trips and chartering a vessel for a custom-designed cruise.

Chateau Whistler Resort

4599 Chateau Boulevard
Mail: Box 100
Whistler, BC V0N 1B0
(604) 938-8000
Fax: (604) 938-2055
Toll-free from Canada: 800-268-9411
Toll-free from U.S.: 800-828-7447

Located 126 kilometres (75 miles) north of Vancouver, at Whistler Village.

Three hundred forty-three rooms and suites: Call for rates.

A full-facility resort hotel that offers downhill and cross-country skiing, hiking, and mountain biking from the front door. This Whistler resort has three tennis courts adjacent to the chateau and a new 18-hole par 72 golf course across the street. The two ski mountains at Whistler, Whistler and Blackcomb, boast the highest vertical in North America. The resort is at the base of the Blackcomb lifts and a short walk from the base of the Whistler lifts. The chateau has a spacious lobby with a peaked 40-foot-high beamed ceiling and a large stone fireplace. A sitting area near the lobby's fireplace, a library-style bar with a fireplace, a large deck, and the main restaurant have views of the mountains and the activity on the ski runs. Rooms and suites have mountain and golf course views, pecan wood furniture, minibars, and TVs. Many are suitable for families, and some are equipped for people with disabilities. The main restaurant features fresh, local, organic ingredients. The hotel has conference facilities (ballrooms, a boardroom, and meeting rooms), a tapas restaurant, a newsstand, sports equipment rentals (including skis, bicycles, and tennis racquets), 12 shops, tennis camps for children, and private tennis lessons. Health club facilities, including an exercise room, indoor and outdoor whirlpools, and an indoor/outdoor pool, have views of the mountains and ski runs. Saunas, steam rooms, and massage therapy are available.

Nancy Greene Lodge

Mail: Box 280
Whistler, BC   V0N 1B0
Whistler: (604) 932-2221
Vancouver: (604) 688-6260
Toll-free from Canada and the U.S.: 800-667-3363

Located in Whistler Village.

Ninety-seven rooms: One or two people $110–155 in winter, $120 in summer.
Forty suites: One or two people $145–170; add'l person $30 in winter; no charge for add'l guests in spring, summer, or fall.
Package rates available.

A modern lodge in the heart of Whistler Village, a few steps from Whistler's skiing and hiking. Boutiques, pubs, mountain bike rentals, a golf course, and convention facilities are within easy walking distance. Accommodation ranges from guest rooms to suites with kitchenettes and fireplaces. The lodge has a heated outdoor pool, indoor and outdoor whirlpools, and a steam room. Two restaurants offer contrasting cuisine—Japanese at Irori and Canadian heritage at Wainwright's.

Durlacher Hof Pension Inn

Peter and Erika Durlacher
7055 Nesters Road
Mail: Box 1125
Whistler, BC V0N 1B0
(604) 932-1924
Fax: (604) 938-1980

One kilometre (1 mile) north of Whistler Village.

Seven rooms: Two people $95–170 in winter, $75–130 in summer,
add'l person $25. Single rates available. Honeymoon suite available.
Skiing, golf, and celebration packages available.

An inn modelled after the farmhouses of the Austrian Alps, with carved balconies and murals. Upstairs, each spacious guest room has hand-carved pine furniture, extra-long queen-sized or twin beds, goose-down duvets, and a private bathroom with Jacuzzi tub or shower. Flowers and Swiss chocolates are provided. Most rooms have balconies and panoramic views of the surrounding peaks. Complimentary multi-course breakfasts. Austrian-style dinners are offered several nights a week. A ground-floor *Bauernstube*, a large, licensed sitting/dining area, has an authentic tile fireplace/oven. Amenities include a sauna, a whirlpool, and a badminton court. Daily maid service, free parking, ski and bike storage. Nearby are skiing, golfing, paragliding, horseback riding, mountain biking, and hiking. The owners arrange sleigh rides, ski tours, heli-tours, and gourmet weekend packages on request. Wheelchair-accessible. Adult oriented. No smoking. No pets. Reservations required. Visa and MasterCard accepted. Selected by Fodor's *Canada's Great Country Inns*, *Best Places to Stay in the Northwest*, *Special Places for Discerning Travellers*, *Unique North West Country Inns*, and *Best Places to Kiss in the Northwest*.

Haus Stephanie Bed and Breakfast

Willi and Doris Weh
7473 Ambassador Crescent
Mail: Box 1460
Whistler, BC   V0N 1B0
(604) 932-5547

Just past the centre of Whistler Village, turn right on Nancy Greene Drive and right again on Ambassador Crescent.

Three rooms: Two people $85 and up, add'l person $20. Summer rates available.

A B&B in a quiet yet convenient location, a ten-minute forest walk from Whistler Village, a seven-minute forest walk from Blackcomb Mountain, and a five-minute walk from cross-country ski trails. Two upstairs bedrooms have queen-sized beds and ensuite washrooms with showers. A bedroom downstairs has twin beds and a private bathroom. Down comforters are provided, and there is an outdoor Jacuzzi. Private entrance for guests. Full breakfast is served in the guest sitting room. No smoking. Deposit of one night's rate required to hold reservation.

Whistler Bed and Breakfast Inns

Toll-free from Canada and the U.S.: 800-665-1892 (for all three inns)

One person $59–89, two people $69–125, add'l person $25, children 7–12 $10.

Edelweiss Pension
7162 Nancy Greene Drive
Mail: Box 850, Whistler, BC   V0N 1B0
(604) 932-3641   Fax: (604) 938-1746

Eight rooms, honeymoon suite with fireplace, licensed living and dining room with fireplace, views, licensed, garden, whirlpool, sauna, special European dinners available. Short walk to lifts and village. No smoking.

Chalet Luise
7461 Ambassador Crescent
Mail: Box 352, Whistler, BC   V0N 1B0
(604) 932-4187   Fax: (604) 938-1531

Eight rooms, honeymoon suites with fireplaces, whirlpool, sauna, garden, special Swiss dinners once or twice a week. Closest pension to lifts and village (walking distance). No smoking.

Carney's Cottage
8106 Cedar Springs Road, Whistler, BC   V0N 1B8
(604) 938-8007   Fax: (604) 938-8023

Eight rooms, ensuite bathrooms, view suite with fireplace, living and dining room with fireplace, outdoor hot tub, sauna, Jacuzzi, dinner available some evenings. No smoking.

Brew Creek Lodge

Peter and Susan Vera
1 Brew Creek Road
Whistler, BC   V0N 1B1
(604) 932-7210
Fax: (604) 932-7223

Brew Creek Lodge is 15 minutes south of Whistler Village. At the Brew Creek Lodge signpost on Highway 99, turn left onto Brew Creek Road and continue for 1 kilometre (1 mile).

Six lodge rooms: One or two people $85, add'1 person $25.
Guest house: One to six people $450, add'1 person $75.
Brew House: One to six people $450, add'1 person $75.

A lodge on two landscaped acres in a wilderness setting 15 minutes from the town of Whistler. The lodge has dining facilities for up to 60 people, a bar, and a sitting area with a large stone fireplace. Each bedroom has a private bathroom. A two-story guest house, which accommodates up to 14 people, has a kitchen, a dining room, a living room, a Jacuzzi, and an executive suite with king-sized bed, fireplace, bathroom, and private entrance. The three-level Brew House, which accommodates up to 12 people, has a kitchen, a dining room, a living room with stone fireplace, a dry sauna, and a Jacuzzi. The living room opens onto a sun deck. A log conference room built over Brew Creek, with a stone fireplace and views of the surrounding forests and mountains, accommodates meetings of up to 30 people. On the grounds are a large outside Jacuzzi, a volleyball court, and a natural swimming pond. Easy access to hiking and biking trails. Tennis, golf, horseback riding, and river rafting in the vicinity.

Bonniebrook Lodge Bed and Breakfast

Karen and Philippe Lacoste
1532 Ocean Beach Esplanade
Mail: RR 4   Site 10   C–34
Gibsons, BC   V0N 1V0
(604) 886-2887

Take the ferry from Horseshoe Bay to Langdale. From the Langdale
ferry terminal, follow Highway 101. Turn left onto Pratt Road, follow it
to the bottom, and turn right onto Gower Point Road. Bonniebrook is at
the foot of Gower Point Road, across from the ocean.

Four rooms: Two people $70–80, add'l person $10.

A 1920s oceanside lodge with a restaurant, Chez Philippe. The restaurant has a rugged
stone fireplace and candlelit tables with flowers and linen. The cuisine is French with
a West Coast influence. Extensive wine list. Sunsets over Georgia Strait from the patio.
On the lodge's upper floor are newly renovated bedrooms. There are three guest bathrooms.
A breakfast including fresh baking is served in the dining room between 8:30 and 10:00
a.m. A large sun deck on the upper floor is for the exclusive use of guests. Given two
kisses in *Best Places to Kiss in the Northwest*. No smoking in the bedrooms. No pets.
Cat in residence.

Lord Jim's Resort Hotel

Hugh and Catherine Gadsby
Ole's Cove Road
Mail: RR 1
Halfmoon Bay, BC   VON 1Y0
(604) 885-7038
Toll-free from Vancouver: 800-681-6168
Fax: (604) 885-7036

From the Langdale ferry terminal, drive about 77 kilometres (48 miles)
north on Highway 101. Then follow signs to Ole's Cove Road and Lord
Jim's.

Eleven rooms: One person $59, two people $72, add'l person $12.
Three suites: One- or two-bedroom or honeymoon $135.
Eleven cabins: One to six people $85–135.
Fishing packages and conference rates offered. Call for details.

A resort on nine acres of rugged land on Malaspina Strait. Lord Jim's is suitable for both
private guests and business groups. Accommodation choices include log cabins among
trees, rooms, and suites. All have ocean views, and most have a private deck or balcony.
In the lodge, a dining room with an ocean view has a menu that specializes in seafood
and fresh regional food. There is live entertainment in a licensed lounge on weekends.
The resort's fishing charters accommodate up to one hundred guests in cabin cruisers
(ideally, four people per cruiser) on half-day, one-day, and two-day packages. Experienced
guides and quality tackle are provided. The chef cooks and serves the catch at dinner or
freezes and boxes it. Conference rates for up to 80 people include use of a meeting room
with audio-visual equipment. The resort has a sauna and, overlooking the ocean, a seasonal
outdoor heated pool, a games room with billiards, and a large barbecue area. Hiking trails,
indoor and outdoor tennis, horseback riding, and golf courses are nearby. No pets.

Mason Road Bed and Breakfast

Joyce Rigaux and John Rayment
5873 Mason Road
Mail: RR 1   TLC Site   C–73
Sechelt, BC   V0N 3A0
(604) 885-3506

Five kilometres (3 miles) north of Sechelt. From Highway 101, turn right onto Nor-West Bay Road and continue to Mason Road. Turn right on Mason Road and drive 1 kilometre (1 mile).

Two rooms: One person $50, two people $75, add'l person $25.
Studio: $90.
Adventure travel tours available. Call for further information.

A new timber-frame house on a 40-acre farm, a few minutes' drive from both Sechelt Inlet and Georgia Strait. Guest rooms in the main house have a separate entrance, private bathrooms and decks, and twin or queen-sized beds with sheep's wool duvets. A detached, self-contained studio, with full kitchen, queen-sized bed, hide-a-bed, and private deck, is suitable for two couples or a family. A breakfast of farm-fresh eggs, fresh berries (in season), homemade muffins, and bread baked in a wood stove is served on the cedar deck or in the guest sitting room/dining room. The farm is home to sheep, chickens, and border collies. There are pesticide-free berry fields, where guests pick their own berries in season. Sheep's wool products are available for purchase. A short drive away, on Sechelt Inlet, is Porpoise Bay Provincial Park, with a beach, a children's play area, and barbecue pits. For scuba divers, Sechelt Inlet offers reefs and a sunken destroyer to explore. Hiking, cycling, golf, tennis, horseback riding, and backcountry skiing are minutes away by car. Adventure travel tours for scuba diving, kayaking, canoeing, sailing, hiking, and cycling available. Children welcome. No pets. No smoking. Cancellation notice seven days.

Mount Daniel Resort (*Maria*)

12881 Highway 101
Mail: Box 22
Madeira Park, BC V0N 2H0
(604) 883-9569
Fax: (604) 883-9569

*From the Langdale ferry terminal, drive 60
kilometres (37 miles) north on Highway 101.
From the Earl's Cove ferry terminal, drive
25 kilometres (16 miles) south on Highway
101.*

Nine self-contained cottages: One or two people $65 and up.
Seven bring-your-own-bedding cabins: One or two people $22.

A family-oriented resort on the Sunshine Coast, close to mountains, lakes, forests, and
the ocean. New self-contained cottages sleep four (one queen-sized bed and one queen-
sized hide-a-bed) or six (one queen-sized bed, two single beds, and one double hide-a-
bed). New, rustic wood cabins have two single beds; guests bring their own bedding and
have the use of washrooms, showers, barbecues, and an open camping kitchen. On site
are a volleyball court, a swimming pool, and a children's playground with a trampoline.
The Sunshine Coast offers diving, saltwater and freshwater fishing, hiking, canoeing, mountain biking, kayaking, boating, windsurfing, and swimming. No smoking.

Sundowner Inn

Mail: Box 113
Garden Bay, BC V0N 1S0
(604) 883-9676
Fax: (604) 883-9886

*Take the ferry from Horseshoe Bay to
Langdale. From the Langdale ferry terminal,
drive north along the Sunshine Coast for
approximately 70 kilometres (45 miles) and
turn left at the Garden Bay resort area sign.
From the Earl's Cove ferry terminal, drive 24 kilometres (16 miles) south. Or fly directly
to the inn by seaplane.*

Twelve rooms: One person $40, two people $45–75.

A restored landmark. Rooms, some with gas fireplaces, overlook Garden Bay. Shared
or private bathrooms. The inn offers West Coast cuisine in its licensed restaurant and has
banquet and meeting facilities, a hot tub, and a gift shop. Nearby activities include boating, scuba diving, golfing, hiking, sailing, kayaking, canoeing, sightseeing, swimming,
and tennis. Pet accommodation available.

Cedar Lodge B&B Resort

Renate and Erwin Schulz
Malaspina Road
Mail: RR 2   C–8
Powell River, BC   V8A 4Z3
(604) 483-4414

Twenty-six kilometres (16 miles) north of Powell River, near the coastal
village of Lund.

Four rooms: One person $40–45; two people, double bed $45–50; two
people, twin beds $50–55. Weekly rates available.
Adventure packages available.

A resort close to Okeover Arm Provincial Park and at the entrance to Desolation Sound
Marine Park. The resort and its wilderness camps are well placed for exploring fjords,
fishing for salmon, and hiking. Each guest room has a two-piece ensuite bathroom. Two
shower rooms are nearby. The resort has a TV and games room, a dining room, a barbecue area, a smoke house, laundry facilities, and a campfire pit. Restaurants are close
by. Guests rent 14-foot boats from the lodge and go on guided fishing and sightseeing
tours. Visa, traveller's cheques, and money orders accepted. No pets.

Don't you guys believe me?

The Harrison Hot Springs Hotel

Harrison Hot Springs, BC   V0M 1K0
(604) 796-2244
Toll-free from Vancouver: (604) 521-8888
Toll-free from Seattle: (206) 622-5736
Toll-free from Pacific Northwest: 800-663-2266
Fax: (604) 796-9374

From Highway 1, turn north onto Highway 9. Three hours' drive from
Seattle or 1½ hours' drive from Vancouver.

Three hundred forty-one rooms: Call for rates.
Many packages available.

A large hot springs resort on the sandy beach of Harrison Lake, with views of lake and mountains. The hotel's saunas and pools, fed by natural mineral springs, are open 24 hours a day. Massage therapists available. Activities include a fitness program, tennis, hiking, water sports, and golf on a nine-hole PGA-rated course. A supervised program for children is offered during holiday periods. One restaurant has a view of the lake and mountains. Another restaurant, which offers dancing to live music, overlooks the outdoor pool and parklike grounds. The hotel has a sitting area with large stone fireplace, a licensed lounge, gift shops, clothing stores, and full convention facilities, including exhibit space, meeting rooms, and catering, for up to six hundred delegates. Harrison Village is a short stroll away.

Manning Park Resort

Manning Park, BC   V0X 1R0
(604) 840-8822
Fax: (604) 840-8848

*On Highway 3, about 45 minutes east of Hope (take exit #177) or 45
minutes west of Princeton.*

Forty lodge rooms, 20 cabins, and 4 chalets: Two people, from $64 in
summer, from $54 in spring/fall, from $70 in winter. Christmas rates
available. Mid-week rates for cabins.

A resort among lodgepole pines four thousand feet above sea level. Manning Provincial
Park is renowned for its hiking, with walks as short as 20 minutes and as long as six
months—the Pacific Crest Trail starts in Manning and ends in southern California. A summer highlight is to walk or hike in subalpine meadows that can be reached by car, one
of the few subalpine meadows in British Columbia with road access; the wildflowers are
in bloom from mid-July to mid-August. The Lightning Lakes area, a 3-kilometre drive
from the resort, offers canoeing, fishing, swimming, strolling, and picnicking. The park
has mountain biking trails and, in winter, downhill skiing facilities and 30 kilometres of
groomed cross-country skiing trails. The lodge has various guest rooms, a cafeteria, and
a dining room. Housekeeping cabins, set back from the lodge, accommodate eight or ten
people. Chalets are tri-plex buildings, each containing two sleeping units and one sleeping unit with kitchen. Each unit sleeps four and can be rented separately (sleeping units
with kitchens are not reserved separately on weekends or holidays). There are two tennis
courts, a horseshoe pitch, a picnic area, a children's playground, and a corral that offers
rides ranging from a one-hour loop to overnight. Meeting and conference facilities are
available.

Cathedral Lakes Lodge

Mail: RR 1
Cawston, BC   V0X 1C0
(604) 499-5848
Fax: (604) 226-7374

Five kilometres (3 miles) west of Keremeos on Highway 3, turn onto
Ashnola River Road and continue for 21 kilometres (13 miles) to the
base camp. A 4-wheel-drive vehicle takes guests 15 kilometres (9 miles)
up a private road to the lodge. Pick-up can be arranged from Keremeos
and from the airport at Penticton.

Lodge and chalet rooms and small and large cabins: Call for rates.
Rates include transportation from base camp to lodge and meals, except
for one large cabin's rates, which do not include meals. Minimum stay
two nights. Open June 15 to October 15.
Watercolour workshops available. Call for more information.

A lodge at 6,800-foot elevation on an alpine lake in Cathedral Provincial Park in the Cas-
cade Mountains. Well-maintained, marked hiking trails radiate from the resort to alpine
meadows, alpine lakes, and mountains. Wildflowers, wildlife, and birds are abundant.
On hikes from the lodge, mountain goats, mule deer, coyotes, marmots, pikas, and, in
late August, California bighorn sheep are often seen. At the lower elevations on the drive
to the lodge, moose, caribou, and black bears are often seen. The lodge arranges guided
hikes and wildlife viewing trips. Use of boats and canoes is included in rates. Watercolour
workshops take place from June to September. There are six rooms upstairs in the main
lodge and four in an adjacent chalet. Small cabins sleep from one to five people; large
cabins sleep up to eight. One large cabin has four bedrooms, a deck, a kitchen, and large
living and dining areas. The rates for the large cabin do not include meals; guests staying
in this cabin may have their meals in the lodge (subject to availability of space) for an
additional charge. The lodge has a large sitting area with massive stone fireplace, a 50-
person dining room, where meals are served buffet style, with complimentary wine at
dinner, and a bar. There is a hot tub. Full payment required 30 days before arrival. Quiet
atmosphere; no TVs or telephones. No smoking. No pets or mountain bikes.

Fossen's Bar 7 Ranch

Louise and Ed Fossen and family
Highway 3 West
Mail: RR 1
Rock Creek, BC   V0H 1Y0
(604) 446-2210

On Highway 3, between Rock Creek and
Bridesville, just west of the Conkle Lake
turnoff.

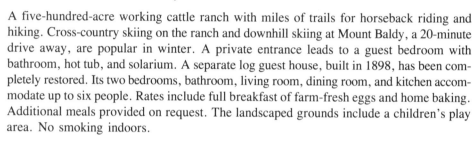

One room: One person $40, two people $50.
Guest house: Two people $65, add'l person $15, child over 10 $10.
Children under 10 free. Weekly rates available.

A five-hundred-acre working cattle ranch with miles of trails for horseback riding and hiking. Cross-country skiing on the ranch and downhill skiing at Mount Baldy, a 20-minute drive away, are popular in winter. A private entrance leads to a guest bedroom with bathroom, hot tub, and solarium. A separate log guest house, built in 1898, has been completely restored. Its two bedrooms, bathroom, living room, dining room, and kitchen accommodate up to six people. Rates include full breakfast of farm-fresh eggs and home baking. Additional meals provided on request. The landscaped grounds include a children's play area. No smoking indoors.

Sol's Bed and Breakfast

Wayne and Sol Klein
Mail: Box 91
Rock Creek, BC   V0H 1Y0
(604) 446-2598

Thirty-five minutes' drive east of Osoyoos on
Highway 3. Turn north onto Johansen Road.
Sol's is the only house on this road.

Two rooms: One person $35, two people
$35–45, add'l person $10.

A turn-of-the-century house that is the hub of a 1,200-acre sheep farm. One guest room has a double bed and one has twin beds. There is a shared bathroom. Breakfast includes homemade bread. Other meals are provided on request. Guests help feed the lambs, ride a wagon out to check the cows, and explore the farm on horseback (horses available) or, in winter, on cross-country skis (guests bring their own equipment). Sol spins and weaves wool from the flock and is happy to share her knowledge. No smoking indoors. Horses can be accommodated.

Sandy Beach Lodge

4275 Mill Road
Mail: Box 8
Naramata, BC V0H 1N0
(604) 496-5765

A 4-hour drive from Vancouver via the Coquihalla Highway. Sixteen
kilometres (10 miles) northeast of Penticton, on Okanagan Lake.

Thirteen log cottages: July and August $1,200–1,300 weekly, June and
September $800–900 weekly, October to May $600–700 weekly. Daily
rates available October to May.
Six lodge rooms: July and August $95 daily, September to June $75
daily.
Long-term rentals and leases available.

A lodge on over two acres of lakefront property with lawns, pines, and maples. A private, 410-foot sandy beach is suitable for swimming, canoeing, sailing, and windsurfing.
A central log lodge has six bedrooms and a sitting room with fireplace and TV. There
is no restaurant on the premises, but several are nearby. Each of the new log cottages
has two bedrooms, a kitchen, a bathroom, beam ceilings, a gas barbecue, and a fireplace.
Shared amenities include two floodlit tennis courts, a heated swimming pool, rowboats
and canoes, a playground, and laundry facilities. Fishing on Okanagan Lake, golfing, and
horseback riding are popular activities. There are several local wineries to visit. Catering
for groups. Listed in *Northwest Best Places*.

Naramata Pines

Jim and Winneth Bence
Juniper Place
Mail: RR 1 Site 14 C-11
Naramata, BC V0H 1N0
(604) 496-5129

*From Penticton, drive 13 kilometres (8 miles)
northeast on Naramata Road. Turn right on
Arawana Road, then left on Debek to Juniper
Drive. Turn left off Juniper Drive onto
Juniper Place.*

Guest rooms: One person $35, two people $45.

A three-story, Tudor-style post and beam country house in a pine forest. A large sitting room has a fireplace. Sun porches on all sides of the house make the most of the views of Okanagan Lake. Guests enjoy hiking and biking close by. The area offers horseback riding, beaches, fishing, farm-gate wineries, and fine dining. Smoking on sun decks only. No pets.

Hatheume Lake Resort

Tim and Janet Tullis, Gus and Leni Averill
Mail: Box 490
Peachland, BC V0H 1X0
(604) 767-2642

Twenty kilometres (12 miles) north of Highway 97C (Okanagan Connector) off the Sunset main exit.

Six cabins: $195–215 per person per day, all-inclusive; children two-thirds rate.

A resort on Hatheume Lake offering a secluded fishing experience. Hatheume Lake Resort was established in 1959 and has been operated by the Averills and Tullises since 1974. A lodge built of hand-hewn logs has a large circular fireplace that separates the family-style dining area from the sitting area. Each of the six two-bedroom log cabins has a living room, a bathroom with shower, and views of the lake. Kamloops trout can often be seen jumping. Available are a four-wheel-drive vehicle to reach eight controlled-access lakes, boats, motors, fuel, fishing and fly casting lessons, tube floating, target golf, mountain bikes, and cleaning, refrigerating, and smoking of fish. Morning coffee and maid service are provided, and ranch-style meals are served in the lodge. Hatheume also hosts a world-renowned fly-fishing school and a distinguished gourmet cooking school. The quality of the resort's hospitality, service, and food has earned praise in *Special Places*, *Best Places to Stay in the Pacific Northwest*, and Fodor's *Canada's Great Country Inns*.

Lake Okanagan Resort

2751 Westside Road
Kelowna, BC   V1Y 8B2
(604) 769-3511
Toll-free from Canada: 800-663-3273
Fax: (604) 769-6665

On the west side of Lake Okanagan, a 20-minute drive from Kelowna.

Two hundred rooms, chalets, and condominiums: Rates range from $75
for two people in low season to $295 for six people in high season.
Children under 14 free.
Special event packages available.

A lakefront resort on three hundred acres of parkland. Various accommodation choices
on a hillside overlook Okanagan Lake. All rooms have kitchenettes, and chalets and condominiums also have fireplaces. The resort has restaurants with lake views, a pub, a lounge,
a poolside bar, convention/meeting facilities, outdoor pools and Jacuzzis with lake views,
seven tennis courts, a par 3 nine-hole golf course, horseback riding, mountain bike rentals, a playground, water sports, marina facilities, and a scuba centre. There is a calendar
of daily activities for children. Packages are offered for events including a tennis tourna-
ment and a wine festival. Local attractions include British Columbia's best vineyards and
fruit farms. Small, house-trained pets permitted—$10 per day to a maximum of $20 per stay.

Earth House Health Retreat Bed and Breakfast

4550 Glenmore Road
Mail: Box 203
Winfield, BC V0H 2C0
(604) 766-2109

Sixteen kilometres (10 miles) north of Kelowna.

Ten rooms: One person $55 and up, two people $65 and up. Weekly
rates available.

A cedar-built B&B retreat on two and a half acres of pine-covered hills, surrounded by
trout lakes, 15 minutes from Kelowna. Ten bedrooms have brass beds, home-made quilts,
and private bathrooms. Quiet atmosphere; no TVs or telephones. Meals are served in a
country-style dining room. Vegetarian food is a specialty. On the patio is a hot tub, just
for guests. Reflexology, shiatsu massage, health appraisals, and nutritional counselling
are available by appointment. Fishing and golfing are close by. Silver Star and Big White
ski areas are within an hour and a half's drive. Smoking outside only. Small pets allowed.

Castle on the Mountain B&B Lodge

Eskil and Sharon Larson
8227 Silver Star Road
Mail: RR 8   Site 10   C–12
Vernon, BC   V1T 8L6
(604) 542-4593

Located 10 kilometres (6 miles) east of
Highway 97.

Five rooms: One person $50–65, two people
$60–85, add'l person $20. Child under 12 $10.

A lodge in a peaceful mountain setting with a panoramic view of city, lakes, and valley. Rooms with double, twin, or queen-sized beds have shared or private bathrooms with showers. A private two-bedroom apartment is also available. For the exclusive use of guests are a sitting room with fireplace and TV, a kitchen, a fire pit, and an outdoor hot tub with a view of stars and city lights. A full Canadian breakfast is included in the rates. The area's attractions include biking, hiking, skiing, beaches, winery tours, bird-watching, and snowmobiling.

The Schroth Farm Bed and Breakfast

Fred and Helen Schroth
3282 East Vernon Road
Mail: RR 8   Site 6   C–25
Vernon, BC   V1T 8L6
(604) 545-0010

One kilometre (1 mile) east of Vernon.

Two rooms: One person $30, two people
$45–55, add'l adult $15, add'l child $10.

A heritage farmhouse with a large patio that has a view of cattle grazing on green pastures against a mountain background. A guest room on the lower floor has twin and double beds, a bathroom, a private entrance, and a private living room with cable TV, VCR, and refrigerator. A guest room on the upper floor has a private bathroom, a TV, and a refrigerator. A country breakfast is served in the sunroom. Sandy beaches for swimming, golf courses, trail riding, a water slide, and a bobslide are nearby. In winter, the nearby slopes of Silver Star offer skiing. Children welcome. Smoking outside only. Wir sprechen Deutsch.

The Pinnacles

9889 Pinnacles Road
Mail: Box 8
Silver Star Mountain, BC   V0E 1G0
(604) 542-4548
(604) 542-8508

From Highway 97 in Vernon, turn east onto 48th Avenue (Silver Star Road) and follow for 22 kilometres (14 miles). Turn left onto Pinnacles Road and follow to its end, 1 kilometre (1 mile).

Twenty-three suites: Ski season $95–295, summer $65–145.

A ski resort in a subalpine setting, 20 minutes' drive from Vernon. Two-, three-, and four-bedroom suites have two or three washrooms, well-equipped kitchens, and sun decks with shared barbecues. Guests reserve private times in roof-top hot tubs and use an indoor swimming pool. By early summer the ski runs that flank the resort turn into flowered meadows that are popular with hikers. Mountain bike rentals and tours, horseback riding, summer chairlift rides, and rollerblade rentals are available at the resort.

Circle-W Hi Hium Fishing Camp

Missy and Ron Bendzak
Deadmans Creek Road
Mail: Box 8
Savona, BC   V0K 2J0
(604) 373-2636

Located in Deadman Valley, between Kamloops and Cache Creek.
Please write or phone for directions.

Eight cabins: $47–67 per person per night, children under 17 half rate.
Includes transportation and rowboat. Minimum stay three nights. Open
mid-May to October. Discounts available.

A secluded fishing camp, with log cabins, oil lamps, wood stoves, and wooden boats.
Guests leave their vehicles at the Circle-W Ranch, where they are offered coffee, iced
tea, and home baking, and are driven to Hi Hium Lake, a one-hour trip in camp vehicles
on a rough, steep, scenic road. Guests then travel by boat to one of the housekeeping
cabins scattered along the lakeshore. Each cabin accommodates parties of up to 10 and
provides everything except food, bedding, and personal items. A wood-heated lakewater
shower and a smokehouse are at each cabin; no power or running water. The lake is known
for its fly-fishing and its Kamloops trout, which weigh up to six pounds. Catch and release
methods are encouraged. Deer, moose, black bears, eagles, and ospreys are often seen.
Advance reservations necessary. No pets. Member of B.C. Fishing Resort and Outfitters
Association.

Lakeside Court Motel

Donn and Margaret Sherman
1001 Savona Access Road
Mail: Box 260
Savona, BC V0K 2J0
(604) 373-2528

Savona is on Highway 1 between Cache Creek and Kamloops; the resort is on Kamloops Lake, 1 kilometre (1 mile) from the highway. Four and a half hours' drive from Vancouver.

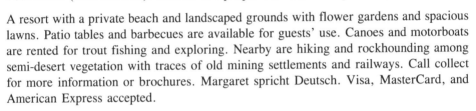

Three rooms: One or two people $60.
Four suites (with kitchens): One or two people $65–70, add'l person $5.

A resort with a private beach and landscaped grounds with flower gardens and spacious lawns. Patio tables and barbecues are available for guests' use. Canoes and motorboats are rented for trout fishing and exploring. Nearby are hiking and rockhounding among semi-desert vegetation with traces of old mining settlements and railways. Call collect for more information or brochures. Margaret spricht Deutsch. Visa, MasterCard, and American Express accepted.

Spruce Grove Wilderness Lodge

The Allenbys
Mail: Box 119
Kamloops, BC V2C 5K9
(604) 398-1362
Fax: (604) 579-8340

From Kamloops, take Westsyde Road north along the Thompson River for 24 kilometres (15 miles). Turn left at Jamieson Creek Road and follow the markers to Bonaparte Lake.

Travel with care on weekdays, as logging trucks use this route.

Six cabins: Two people $40.50–50.50, add'l person $5. Bedding and towels extra. Family rates available. American plan: one person $120, two people $200.
Tent sites and RV sites available.

Rustic light housekeeping cabins on the east end of Bonaparte Lake. The cabins are furnished and have cooking facilities and refrigerators. Electricity is available for 10 hours per day. A central building has hot showers and flush toilets. The lodge has a fully licensed lounge and dining area. Guests buy sandwich bar lunches at any time of day. Breakfast and dinner are booked a day in advance. Guests fish, hunt, mountain bike, and explore the Lupin Lake chain by canoe. Mountain bike, canoe, boat, motor, and tackle rentals are available, as are boat launching facilities, fishing licences, and hunting guide service. There is a sandy beach nearby. Cancellation notice 15 days. Visa accepted.

Quaaout Lodge

Paul LeClerc
Mail: Box 1215
Chase, BC V0E 1M0
(604) 679-3090
Toll-free: 800-663-4303
Fax: (604) 679-3039

On Shuswap Lake, 7 kilometres (4 miles) east of Chase and 43 kilometres (27 miles) west of Salmon Arm. Access via the Squilax Bridge over the Little South Thompson River.

Seventy-two rooms: November 1 to May 31, one person $60–75, two people $70–85; June 1 to October 31, one person $77–89, two people $92–107; add'l person $15. Corporate, government, and weekend rates available.

Seven tepees in summer: $10–15 per person (maximum 10 people per tepee).

A new resort built by the Little Shuswap Indian Band with assistance from the federal government's Native Economic Development Fund and the All-Nations' Trust. The Salish word *quaaout*, ''where the sun's rays first touch the land,'' aptly describes Quaaout Lodge's position on the shore of Little Shuswap Lake. Most guest rooms have two double beds. Twelve rooms with king-sized beds have kitchenettes, and six suites with king-sized beds have Jacuzzis and fireplaces. Three rooms are suitable for people with disabilities. Tepees are available during summer months. The lodge has a licensed dining room, an indoor swimming pool, a sauna, a whirlpool, a gift shop, an outdoor barbecue deck, and a patio. There are meeting/banquet rooms for large functions. Authentic native dishes are featured on all menus. Summer activities include canoeing, water-skiing, windsurfing, cycling, and hiking. The resort has 12 kilometres of prepared walking trails and 3 kilometres of jogging trails with fitness steps. The salmon run that takes place every fall in the Adams River is minutes from the lodge. Winter activities include alpine skiing at Tod Mountain, cross-country skiing at the lodge, sleigh riding, and snowmobiling.

The Loon's Nest Bed and Breakfast

Sigrid Arnold
2506 Reedman Point Road
Mail: General Delivery
Blind Bay, BC V0E 1H0
(604) 675-2074
Fax: (604) 675-2074

On Shuswap Lake, 21 kilometres (13 miles) west of Salmon Arm, 9 kilometres (6 miles) east of Sorrento. From Highway 1, turn north onto Balmoral Road and travel 6 kilometres (4 miles) to Reedman Point.

Two rooms: One person $35, two people $45–50. Weekly rates available.

A modern cedar bungalow with an English-style country garden, in a quiet rural setting overlooking Blind Bay on Shuswap Lake. Rooms have queen-sized beds and share a private sitting room. A sauna and hot tub provide relaxation. Breakfast is tailored to guests' tastes and is likely to include local cheeses, farm-fresh eggs, fruit, and homemade breads. A number of Shuswap Lake's beaches are a five-minute walk away. The area offers fishing, boating, hiking, bicycling, horseback riding, golfing, and viewing the Adams River salmon run. Cross-country skiing in winter. German and French spoken. Smoking outside only.

Llama Lane Bed and Breakfast

Kathy and Gerry Flucke
2828 Forbes Road
Salmon Arm, BC V1E 4M1
(604) 832-9398
Fax: (604) 832-9398

From Salmon Arm, travel south on Salmon
Valley Road for 21 kilometres (13 miles),
then west on Forbes Road.

Guest house: One or two people $60, add'l person $10.
Small cottage: One person $35, two people $45.

A B&B with 25 acres of woodland and pasture for resident llamas, a salmon-spawning river, and an abundance of wildflowers, birds, and small wildlife. A guest house has a full kitchen, a bathroom, a bedroom with queen-sized bed, a sitting/dining area with pull-out sofa, and a large deck. A cottage has a bedroom with two single beds and a bathroom. The guest house and cottage are winterized. Breakfast is served in the hosts' house or on their deck or patio. The Shuswap area is known for its lakes, houseboating, fishing, and golf. Nearby Mount Ida Provincial Forest offers many miles of hiking trails. Cross-country and alpine skiing are popular winter activities. Smoking outside only. Inquire first about pets.

Gleneden Bales Bed and Breakfast

Lynn Halliwell
5771 – 40th Street NW
Salmon Arm, BC V1E 4M2
(604) 832-6438

From Salmon Arm, take Highway 1 west to
50th Avenue. Turn left. Continue to 40th
Street. Turn right. Continue to sixth driveway
on left and follow this lane to the end.

Two rooms: One person $40–50, two people $50–60.
Box stalls for horses: $10, including bedding; $20, including hay, bedding, and cleaning. Lower rates available for longer stays. Weekly and off-season rates available October to April.

A log house on a 20-acre farm. All rooms have views of Shuswap Lake and the town of Salmon Arm. Guests have a private entrance and large living room/library. A large bedroom has an ensuite bathroom and TV. A smaller bedroom has twin beds, duvets, and a bathroom (shower only) across the hall. Juice, coffee, and fresh baking are served in the living room an hour before a full farm breakfast on a covered sun deck. Riding, hiking, and cross-country ski trails begin at the farm. Beach, golf courses, and tennis courts are close by. Two dogs, two cats, and three thoroughbred horses are in residence. Facilities available for equine guests.

Waterway Houseboat Vacations

John Vinje
113 Weddup Street
Mail: Box 69
Sicamous, BC V0E 2V0
(604) 836-2505
Toll-free: 800-663-4022

*Located midway between Vancouver and Calgary at the intersection of
Highway 1 and Highway 97A. Five hours' drive from Calgary,
Vancouver, and Spokane; 8 hours' drive from Edmonton and Seattle.*

Forty-eight houseboats: Packages $569 and up. Minimum stay two
nights. Open April to October.

Houseboating holidays on the Shuswap Lake system. The Shuswap is a houseboating resort,
with sandy beaches, quiet coves, and lakeshore activities including dining, golfing, horseback riding, and hiking. Each houseboat has a private stateroom, a penthouse suite, a
bathroom, a microwave oven, a generator, a stereo, a ship-to-shore radio, a water slide,
and a barbecue. Some have upper-deck Jacuzzis. The staff's thorough briefing, which
includes an instructional video, an overview of the lake system, and on-board orientation,
ensures that houseboat captains will feel confident, even at the helm of the largest (56-
foot) vessel.

Wells Gray Park Backcountry Chalets

Ian Eakins and Tay Briggs
Mail: Box 188
Clearwater, BC   V0E 1N0
(604) 674-3317
Fax: (604) 674-3387

Chalets: $25 per person in summer, $30 in winter.
Cabins: $15 per person.
Hut-to-hut skiing and hiking packages, canoeing packages, and other packages available. Call for details.

A four-hut system (two chalets and two cabins) on a 50-kilometre-long alpine plateau in Wells Gray Park that enables hikers and skiers to enjoy a vast wilderness of mountains, alpine meadows, forests, streams, and lakes. Mountain caribou, deer, bears, many other mammals, and birds are often seen. The chalets are equipped with propane heat and stoves, kitchens, mattresses, and blankets. The cabins are more rustic but comfortable. Guests stay in one chalet and explore from there or hike (in summer) or backcountry ski (in winter) from hut to hut. Packages include meals and professional guides. Alternatively, the huts can be rented on an accommodation-only basis. The huts are remote: they are reached in summer by a two-hour hike and in winter by either a helicopter ride or a three-hour ski. Guided canoeing trips are available on a major lake system in the park; call for details.

Monashee Chalet

Adolf Teufele
Mail: Interior Alpine Recreation Ltd.
Box 1528
Kamloops, BC   V2C 6L8
(604) 522-1239
Fax: (604) 522-1239

Approximately 2½ hours' drive north of Kamloops, near Blue River.
Accessible by hiking, skiing, or snowcat.

Backcountry chalet: $30 per person, groups of 9–14 $27 per person,
children 7–12 half rate. Children under 7 free. January special: $20 per
person.
Open December 15 to May 16 and August 1 to October 15.
Gourmet package and guided backcountry skiing and hiking packages
available: Call for rates.
Transportation by snowcat: Call for rates.

A backcountry chalet at six-thousand-foot elevation in the Monashee Mountains, providing a base for backcountry ski touring, alpine hiking, and rock climbing. The chalet accomo-
dates up to 14 guests in seven sleeping compartments with futon mattresses and lofts for
children. Guests bring their own bedding. The chalet has wood heat, an electric generator
for light, gas lanterns, an indoor shower, an outdoor toilet, and a kitchen with wood and
propane stoves. A gourmet package includes all meals. The best skiing conditions are from
November to May. The varied terrain is suitable for all ages and skill levels. Summer
and fall are the prime seasons for hiking among alpine meadows and mountain climbing.
A radio telephone is available near the chalet. Guests bring their own skiing and climbing
equipment. Guide service optional. In summer, the chalet is reached by hiking 3 kilometres
(approximately 45 to 60 minutes). In winter, the chalet is reached by skiing 14 kilometres
along a trail (approximately five hours) or by snowcat ride (approximately 90 minutes).
Guests who wish to ski in with a lighter load have their packs and food supplies brought
by the snowcat. Non-refundable deposit of $30 per person required to hold reservation;
balance due 45 days before arrival.

Dave Henry Lodge

Headwaters Outfitting Ltd.
Liz Norwell and Brian McKirdy
1030 Whisky Fill Road
Mail: Box 818
Valemount, BC   V0E 2Z0
(604) 566-4718

Headwaters Outfitting is located 3 kilometres (2 miles) south of Valemount on Whisky Fill Road.

Winter: $30 per person ($75 catered), helicopter $90 one way.

Summer: Catered riding packages, four days $495 per person, five days $595, eight days $840. Children 15% discount.

A log lodge in the Rockies, surrounded by alpine flowers and sparkling lakes. At the headwaters of Dave Henry Creek on the western edge of Mount Robson Provincial Park, the lodge is accessible only by riding, hiking, skiing, or helicopter. Home-cooked meals, wood heat, wood-fired sauna, no indoor plumbing. Guests bring their own sleeping bags unless other arrangements are made. From the lodge, guests take guided riding and hiking trips into Jasper National Park and Mount Robson Park and along the Great Divide. In winter, the terrain around the lodge is suitable for telemarking. Both catered/guided and self-catered/self-guided rates available. No pets.

Ram's Head Inn

Red Mountain Road
Mail: Box 636
Rossland, BC   V0G 1Y0
(604) 362-9577
Fax: (604) 362-5399

Rossland is approximately 30 kilometres (19 miles) south of Castlegar on Highway 3A.

Twelve rooms: One person $55; two people, queen-sized bed or twin beds $65; two people, king-sized bed $110.

An inn at the base of the Red Mountain ski area. The inn's unassuming exterior conceals a well-appointed, relaxing place for couples and adult families who enjoy outdoor activities. All bedrooms have duvets and private bathrooms. Breakfast is served in front of the main room's stone fireplace. Nearby are mountain biking, golfing, downhill and cross-country skiing, gold mine tours, the Rossland Historic Mining Museum, and Rossland's historical sites. For guests' use are a teak hot tub under tall pines and a sauna. Recommended by *Northwest Best Places*. Visa, MasterCard, American Express, and Discover accepted. No smoking.

Kootenay Creations Bed and Breakfast

David Shadbolt and Sophia Andras-Shadbolt
6996 Highway 3A
Mail: RR 3
Nelson, BC   V1L 5P6
(604) 229-5413

On Highway 3A, 5 minutes' drive west of the Balfour ferry terminal or 25 minutes' drive east of Nelson.

Four rooms: One person $45-60, two people $55-70.

A spacious cedar lodge on the shore of the west arm of Kootenay Lake. Two living rooms, one with TV and one with books, are shared with hosts. Large picture windows and a sun deck have views of forested hills, ospreys and eagles, fish jumping, and ducks feeding. There are fireplaces and a sauna. Nearby are hiking, cycling, golfing, fishing, and sailing. Sightseeing is varied, from Kootenay Lake and Kokanee Glacier to the heritage buildings of Nelson and long-deserted mining towns. Ainsworth Hot Springs is nearby. Breakfast is served in a dining area overlooking the lake. No smoking.

Svensen's Farm Bed and Breakfast

Cathryn and Larry Svensen
374 Old Mill Road
Mail: SS 1   Site 21   C-9
Fruitvale, BC   V0G 1L0
(604) 367-9624

One kilometre (1 mile) east of Fruitvale, which lies on Highway 3B.

Guest house: Two people $60–70, four to six people $100.
Main house (two rooms): One person $30.
Stay seven nights; pay for six.

A 12-acre organic farm with turkeys, chickens, ducks, rabbits, sheep, goats, a horse, and the occasional wild deer. The farm is quiet and private without being isolated. Guests milk goats, shear sheep, collect eggs, and relax in hammocks with books from the farm's library. Guests staying in the main house share a den and patio with the hosts and have an upstairs verandah for their private use. The guest house has a bedroom, a kitchen, a dining area, a living room, TV/VCR, videos, and a library. Breakfast is served in the main house. Eggs, produce, fruit, and walnuts are fresh from the farm. Picnic lunches, extra meals, and vegetarian menus can be arranged. Horseback riding, fishing, golfing, and cross-country and downhill skiing are nearby. Smoking on the patio only. Pets must be leashed or caged—pens available.

Bull River Guest Ranch

Josef and Margit Eitzenberger
Mail: Box 133
Cranbrook, BC V1C 4H7
(604) 429-3760

*From Fort Steele (10 minutes from Cranbrook), turn onto Fort Steele–
Wardner Road and drive for 24 kilometres (15 miles). At the power
plant, turn north onto the gravel road. Continue for 12 kilometres (7
miles). There are signs from Fort Steele on. In Cranbrook, car rental
and pick-up service are available.*

Seven log chalets: One person $48, add'l person $10, child 5–11 $5,
children under 5 free.

A working cattle ranch in its own mountain valley. Each self-contained alpine-style log
chalet has a view from the front porch, a fireplace, electricity, and a shower. There is
an unlicensed saloon. Guests ride the open range with the ranch crew, watch the farm
animals, and go fishing, swimming, and boating. Trails lead through field and forest to
nearby lakes (canoes available) and mountains. Elks, deer, bears, beavers, and eagles are
often seen. Afternoon trips can be made to Fort Steele, Kimberley (the Bavarian-style
city of the Rockies), and the railway museum in Cranbrook that was pulled to Vancouver
for Expo '86. The ranch provides a base for day trips to Kootenay Park, Kootenay Lake,
Radium Hot Springs, Banff, Nelson, Waterton Park, and the cattle auctions in Pincher
Creek. Washington, Idaho, and Montana can all be visited in one day. The Prairies can
be visited in another day. AAA recommended.

Top of the World Guest Ranch

Mail: Box 29
Fort Steele, BC   V0B 1N0
(604) 426-6306

Ten kilometres (6 miles) northeast of Fort Steele.

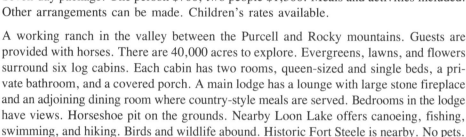

Three-day package: One person $400, two people $710.
Five-day package: One person $560, two people $1,020.
Seven-day package: One person $700, two people $1,300. Meals and activities included. Other arrangements can be made. Children's rates available.

A working ranch in the valley between the Purcell and Rocky mountains. Guests are provided with horses. There are 40,000 acres to explore. Evergreens, lawns, and flowers surround six log cabins. Each cabin has two rooms, queen-sized and single beds, a private bathroom, and a covered porch. A main lodge has a lounge with large stone fireplace and an adjoining dining room where country-style meals are served. Bedrooms in the lodge have views. Horseshoe pit on the grounds. Nearby Loon Lake offers canoeing, fishing, swimming, and hiking. Birds and wildlife abound. Historic Fort Steele is nearby. No pets.

Timbers Resort

John and Mabel Daniels
Columbia Lake
Mail: Box 38
Fairmont Hot Springs, BC   V0B 1L0
(604) 345-6636

Located off Highway 93/95, 7 kilometres (4 miles) south of Fairmont Hot Springs on Columbia Road.

Seven cottages: One person $40, two people $45–55, add'l person $5.
Four RV sites: $10 per vehicle, $1 for power.
Open May to September.

A resort in a quiet mountain setting with tall trees. Self-contained cottages have one or two bedrooms and showers. Some of the cottages have fireplaces. The resort has lots of space for running and playing, swings, a horseshoe pit, a fire pit, and a barbecue. Columbia Lake, a five-minute walk away, offers fishing and boating. Hiking and trail riding are nearby, and there are many golf courses in the area.

Fairmont Hot Springs Resort

Mail: Box 10
Fairmont Hot Springs, BC V0B 1L0
(604) 345-6311
Fax: (604) 345-6616
Toll-free: 800-663-4979

Located on Highway 93/95, 1¾ hours' drive southwest of Banff.

One hundred forty rooms: One or two people, January 3 to April 8, November 1 to December 22, $60–70; April 9 to May 20, October 12 to 31, $85–95; May 21 to October 10, December 23 to January 2, $115–120.

Two hundred sixty-five RV sites: $14–18.

Golf-and-swim, spa, romance, and family packages offered.

A resort where guests swim and relax in the waters of Canada's largest odorless mineral hot pools. Massage and hydro-therapy services are available. On-site gift stores carry a wide selection of swimwear. Rooms in the lodge enjoy views of the Rockies or the pools. Restaurants provide a choice of casual dining, dining and dancing, or pub-style meals. A licensed lounge offers nightly entertainment. The resort has two golf courses: rugged Mountainside and gentler Riverside. Riverside incorporates the Columbia River as one of its hazards. Golf-and-swim packages allow guests unlimited golf (mid-week). In winter, the resort has its own ski area, and there are tennis courts and hiking trails. Family recreation packages include supervised children's activities and free accommodation for children under 14. Facilities for conventions or events for up to three hundred people. Adjacent two-thousand-metre airstrip.

Windermere Creek Bed and Breakfast

Scott and Astrid MacDonald
1658 Windermere Loop Road
Mail: Box 409
Windermere, BC   V0B 2L0
(604) 342-0356

From Windermere, travel south on Highway 95/93 for 1 kilometre (1 mile) to the south end of Windermere Loop Road. Turn left and follow the Loop Road past the Windermere Valley Golf Course. Third house on the right, across the street from the northeast corner of the golf course.

Four rooms: One or two people $60.
Cabin: $85.
Open May to October. Open in winter by arrangement.

A B&B on 107 forested acres with lawns, gardens, walking trails, a heated pool, creek-side hammocks, beaver ponds, and various picnic/lookout spots. Guest accommodation is on the main floor of the house. Besides the bedrooms, there are two bathrooms, a living room with fireplace, a dining room, a sunroom with deck, and a breakfast nook with wood stove. A cold buffet breakfast is served. A heritage cabin (c. 1890) has been refurbished. Another heritage cabin (non-sleeping) has been restored and offers a place for sitting and relaxing. Nearby are Radium Hot Springs and Fairmont Hot Springs, with their pools and golfing. Invermere on the Lake and Windermere's public beach and art shops are five minutes' drive away. Not suitable for children. Restricted smoking.

Addison's Bungalows

Larry and Arleen Reid
Mail: Box 56
Radium Hot Springs, BC   V0A 1M0
(604) 347-9545
Fax: (604) 347-9511

Located inside the west gate of Kootenay National Park on the north side of Highway 93.

Twenty-four bungalows: One to eight people $32–105.
Six motel rooms: One to four people $42–69.
Senior, group, and weekly rates available.

A resort adjacent to the pools of Radium Hot Springs, with bungalows scattered among mature Douglas fir trees. Twenty bungalows have all-wood interiors, open beam ceilings, and stone fireplaces; each contains linen, dishes, cutlery, pots, pans, toaster, hot plate, refrigerator, TV, and bathroom with shower. Each of the other four bungalows has a combined living room and kitchen with acorn fireplace, separate bedrooms, and a bathroom with tub and shower. Motel rooms have queen-sized beds, TVs, and bathrooms with tub and shower. There are barbecue areas, a playground, and a small confectionery. Rocky Mountain bighorn sheep stroll down the streets and keep the grass trimmed. Nearby hiking trails lead to the Sinclair Canyon waterfall. Golfing, whitewater rafting, swimming, boating, fishing, horseback riding, and naturalist tours are within a short driving distance. Pets allowed. Visa and MasterCard accepted.

Kootenay Park Lodge

(formerly Vermilion Crossing Bungalows)
Paul V. Holscher, General Manager
Mail: Box 1390
Banff, AB T0L 0C0
(403) 762-9196
Fax: (403) 262-5028

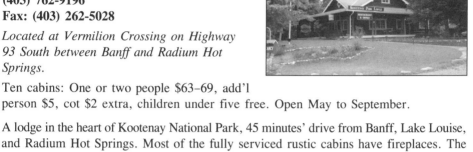

Located at Vermilion Crossing on Highway
93 South between Banff and Radium Hot
Springs.

Ten cabins: One or two people $63–69, add'l
person $5, cot $2 extra, children under five free. Open May to September.

A lodge in the heart of Kootenay National Park, 45 minutes' drive from Banff, Lake Louise, and Radium Hot Springs. Most of the fully serviced rustic cabins have fireplaces. The lodge has a sitting area with a large fireplace. A restaurant featuring home-style cooking has been praised by a CBC-Calgary food critic. Grocery store and gas station on site. Many hiking trails begin nearby. Wildlife is often seen in the area. The lodge is a convenient spot for cyclists on the Golden Triangle route. Fishing, whitewater rafting, camping, and mountain biking are popular activities. Pets allowed. Visa, MasterCard, and Enroute accepted. Reservations recommended. Cancellation notice three days.

Columbia Valley Lodge

Erwin Perzinger
Mail: Box 2669
Golden, BC V0A 1H0
(604) 348-2508
Fax: (604) 348-2508

On Highway 95, 23 kilometres (14 miles)
south of Golden, on the way to Radium Hot
Springs. A 1-hour drive from Rogers Pass, a
45-minute drive from Lake Louise, a 1½-hour
drive from Banff.

Twelve rooms: One person $35; two people, double bed $45; two
people, twin beds $54; add'l person $5. Discounts for longer stays and
for seniors.

A European-style lodge surrounded by the Rocky Mountains, the Purcell Mountains, and the Columbia Valley wetlands. All rooms are quiet and have private bath/shower. Some rooms have balconies, some have TVs, and some are designated non-smoking. European and Canadian cuisine is prepared by an Austrian chef and served in a licensed dining room. Limited menu. Nearby activities include canoeing (canoes available for rent), bird-watching, and horseback riding. No pets. Reservations preferred. Visa and MasterCard accepted.

Beaverfoot Lodge

Don Wolfenden
Mail: Box 1560
Golden, BC V0A 1H0
(604) 344-7144

Just outside Yoho National Park. From Golden, drive east on Highway 1 for 28 kilometres (17 miles). Turn south on Beaverfoot Forestry Road (gravel) and continue for 13 kilometres (8 miles).

Nine lodge rooms: Adult $85 ($425 weekly), child 6–12 $55 ($275 weekly), child under 6 $30 ($125 weekly).
Twenty covered wagons: Adult $75 daily.
Rates include meals, guided hiking, horseback riding, canoeing, and fishing. Bed and breakfast rates also available.
Three-day guided horseback/hiking trip, including meals, one night in a cabin, and two nights in a tent: $300. Call for details. Early booking required.

A remote wilderness resort in the Rockies, with a log lodge, 20 covered wagons, and a backcountry cabin, offering guided hiking, horseback riding, canoeing, and fishing, all from the front door of the resort. The lodge has a sitting room with a central fireplace and a dining room. Guests staying in the lodge share bathrooms. Covered wagons each house two people, with shared bathrooms nearby. Guests staying in the wagons have their meals in a covered outdoor dining area. Log saunas, heated by wood, are convenient to both the lodge and the wagons. There is whitewater rafting on the Kickinghorse River nearby. In winter, the lodge and the backcountry ski-in cabin are open, and there are 90 kilometres of groomed and tracked trails for cross-country skiing (December 15 to April 1).

Purcell Lodge

ABC Wilderness Adventures Ltd.
Mail: Box 1829
Golden, BC V0A 1H0
(604) 344-2639

In the remote backcountry of the British Columbia Rockies between
Glacier National Park and Yoho National Park. Access by helicopter
from Golden (year-round) or by hiking trail (late June to October).

Ten rooms: Adventure packages $99–205 per person per night.

A lodge offering hotel-calibre service in a remote mountain setting. Surrounded by mountains and glaciers, the resort provides doorstep access to extensive hiking areas in alpine meadows. All rooms have mountain views. The lodge has a licensed dining room, a living room with fireplace, a reading room, and a sauna. Winter activities include cross-country and telemark skiing, tobogganing, and snowshoeing. Packages include meals and guiding and naturalist (or ski instruction) services. No smoking. No children under 12. Advance reservations only. Minimum stay two nights. Visa, MasterCard, American Express.

Golden Alpine Holidays

Mail: Box 1050
Golden, BC V0A 1H0
(604) 344-7273

*Located in the Esplanade Range of the Selkirk Mountains. Helicopter
pick-up point is a an hour's drive northwest of Golden.*

Three lodges: Three nights $479 per person, four nights $570, six
nights $710, seven nights $787. Rates include helicopter, meals, and
guide service.

Three lodges beside a lake in a high hanging valley accessible only by helicopter. Between
July and September, guests hike from lodge to lodge through unspoiled alpine wilderness.
Between December and April, choices include lodge-to-lodge ski-touring, telemarking,
and randonée. Each lodge has six bedrooms with double beds upstairs and a bright, open
common room on the ground floor. Meals are cooked on a wood stove and served family
style around a large table. There is a homesteading feel—no indoor plumbing or electricity, and only propane light. No age or ability restrictions.

Emerald Lake Lodge

Mail: Box 10
Field, BC   V0A 1G0
(604) 343-6321
Toll-free: 800-663-6336
Fax: (604) 343-6724

Located in Yoho National Park, an hour's drive west of Banff along Highway 1. From Field, follow signs to Emerald Lake.

Eighty-five units: Two people $100–285, add'l person $15.

A lodge with 24 new cabin-style buildings, on a lake among rugged peaks in the Rockies. The hand-hewn timber lodge, built by the Canadian Pacific Railway in 1902 and extensively renovated in 1986, has preserved its original character. It has a formal dining room, quiet reading and sitting rooms, a games room, and a lounge with an oak bar from an 1890s Yukon saloon. Large stone fireplaces. The cabin-style buildings have been designed to fit in with the traditional architecture of the original lodge. Spacious guest rooms have double or queen-sized beds with duvets, antique furniture, fieldstone fireplaces, and private balconies with views of the lake. There are no TVs or radios, and the parking lot is away from the lodge itself (shuttle service is provided). A short distance from the lodge are a 14-foot outdoor hot tub, a sauna, and an exercise room. Several rooms, ranging from a boardroom for 10 to reception rooms for 100, are available for conferences and social functions. Canoeing, cross-country skiing, hiking, and fishing are popular. The downhill ski slopes at Lake Louise are 40 kilometres away, and the Burgess shale fossil beds are nearby.

Baker Creek Chalets & Bistro

Mike, Jan, and Kirby Huminuik
Mail: Box 66
Lake Louise, AB T0L 1E0
(403) 522-3761
Fax: (403) 522-2270

Located on the Bow Valley Parkway (1A) between Lake Louise and Banff, 10 kilometres (6 miles) from Lake Louise and 40 kilometres (25 miles) from Banff.

Twenty-five chalets: Two people $80–115, four people $135, add'l person $10.

Log chalets and a creekside log lodge, all recently constructed, in a quiet wilderness setting among trees and wildflowers in Banff National Park. One-room chalets have kitchenettes; two-bedroom chalets and one-bedroom chalets with lofts have kitchens. All have fireplaces, decks, red roofs, and hand-painted flowers on red shutters. Quiet atmosphere; no TVs or telephones. In the lodge, a bistro restaurant with a sun deck and two stone fireplaces is open in summer for breakfast, lunch, and dinner and in winter for dinner on Fridays, Saturdays, and Sundays only. Besides visiting Banff National Park's many attractions by car, guests cycle, fish, canoe, and hike (short hikes to a three-day loop hike into the mountains) and, in winter, cross-country ski and snowshoe, all from their front doors. In fall the larch trees are golden. September is elk rutting season. Downhill skiing and skating at Lake Louise are 10 minutes away by car. The resort is included in Fodor's *Canada's Great Country Inns* and has recently been awarded the Alberta Tourism Housekeeping Award. The restaurant is listed in *Where to Eat in Canada*. Deposit of one night's rate required to hold reservation.

Lake Louise Inn

210 Village Road
Mail: Box 209
Lake Louise, AB   T0L 1E0
(403) 522-3791
Toll-free from western Canada and the U.S.: 800-661-9237
Fax: (403) 522-2018

A five-minute walk from the village of Lake Louise.

Two hundred twenty-two rooms and suites: $70–160, depending on season and type of room.

Two-, three-, and five-day skiing packages and health and fitness spa weeks.

An inn close to ski areas at Lake Louise, Sunshine Village, Mystic Ridge, and Norquay and to hiking trails, horseback riding, canoeing, and fishing. Some rooms have queen-sized beds and balconies. Family units have kitchens and fireplaces. Executive suites have kitchenettes, fireplaces, and balconies. The inn has a dining room, a patio (where a bar-becue is offered), a licensed lounge, a pizzeria, a pub, a heated indoor pool, a whirlpool, and a sauna. Spring and fall are particularly popular for retreats, seminars, and conferences.

Moraine Lake Lodge

Summer mailing address: Box 70
Lake Louise, AB   T0L 1E0
June to September: (403) 522-3733
October to May: (403) 762-4401 or (toll-
free) 800-661-8340
Fax: (403) 762-5905
Winter mailing address: Box 1017,
Banff, AB   T0L 0C0

Located 11 kilometres (7 miles) southwest of
Lake Louise.

Eight lodge rooms: One or two people $130–170, add'l person $25.
Eighteen cabin suites: One or two people $160–215, add'l person $25.
Open June to September.

A lodge designed by one of Canada's best-known architects, Arthur Erickson, to comple-
ment its location on the edge of unspoiled Moraine Lake in the Valley of the Ten Peaks.
Each cabin has a view, a sunken living room with fireplace, king-sized or twin beds, and
a private deck. Lodge rooms overlook the lake and have one queen-sized or two double
beds. A living room/library, where complimentary afternoon tea is served, has huge timbers, a stone fireplace, and view windows. A restaurant and cafeteria cater to all tastes.
Guests hike and explore the lake by canoe (canoes available). Deposit of one night's rate
required within 14 days of booking to hold reservation. Visa, MasterCard, and American
Express accepted.

Mountaineer Lodge

101 Village Road
Mail: Box 150
Lake Louise, AB   T0L 1E0
(403) 522-3844
Fax: (403) 522-3902

In the village of Lake Louise, 4 kilometres (2
miles) from the lake.

Seventy-eight rooms: One person $50–160,
two people $55–160, one- to three-room
family units $75–160. Off-season rates and family plan available. Open May to October.

A lodge in Lake Louise, with many rooms designed for families. Complimentary tea and
coffee are served in the morning, and satellite movies are provided in the rooms. The
lodge has a whirlpool and steam room. Restaurants, shops, and services are close by.
Hiking, canoeing, horseback riding, and sightseeing are popular nearby activities. Bears,
elks, and deer are often seen on the grounds. Wheelchair accessible. No pets. One non-
smoking floor. Alberta Tourism Housekeeping Award winner.

Rundlestone Lodge

Bill Frankish
537 Banff Avenue
Mail: Box 489
Banff, AB T0L 0C0
(403) 762-2201
Fax: (403) 762-4501

Eighty rooms: Two people $105–135 in summer, $45–65 in winter.

A lodge five blocks from Banff's commercial centre. The lodge is finished in stucco and stone and has log balconies and a lobby with a massive stone fireplace. Accommodation choices range from a room with queen-sized bed to an executive suite with a whirlpool, a fireplace, a kitchen, and a loft with king-sized bed. Two rooms have been designed for people using wheelchairs. Complimentary Continental breakfast in the summer months. Facilities include underground parking, elevator, indoor whirlpool, and sauna. The lodge is next to a park, and there are four restaurants within a block.

Banff Ptarmigan Inn

337 Banff Avenue
Mail: Box 1840
Banff, AB T0L 0C0
(403) 762-2207
Toll-free: 800-661-8310
Fax: (403) 762-3577

On the main street in Banff.

One hundred forty-five rooms: One person $50–148, two people $60–158, add'l person $10, children under 12 free.

A heritage resort that offers superb balcony views of the Rocky Mountains and is a short walk from the shopping and night life of downtown Banff. Guest rooms have pine furniture and down-filled comforters. The resort has two restaurants, a licensed lounge with pool table and TVs, a sauna, a large whirlpool, exercise facilities, and a gift shop. A masseuse is in residence. Childcare available. Non-smoking rooms.

Canadian Mountain Holidays

Mail: Box 1660
Banff, AB T0L 0C0
(403) 762-7100
Toll-free: 800-661-0252
Fax: (403) 762-5879

Canadian Mountain Holidays offers hiking and walking vacation packages from three remote mountain lodges, Cariboo, Bugaboo and Bobbie Burns. Guests reach the lodge of choice by helicopter and explore unspoiled wilderness in a small group led by a knowledgeable guide. All levels of fitness and experience welcome. Each day's activity is tailored to the interests of the guests. Non-refundable deposit of $200 required to hold reservation; balance due eight weeks before arrival. Phone for details on lodge-to-lodge trips.

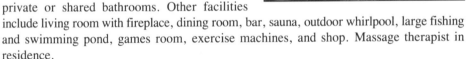

Cariboo Lodge

Ernst Buehler

Located 125 kilometres (80 miles) southwest of Jasper National Park. The heliport is 4 kilometres (2 miles) south of Valemount, B.C.

One-day to five-night packages: $203–1,722 per person. Children's rates available.

Cariboo Lodge has rooms with double beds and private or shared bathrooms. Other facilities include living room with fireplace, dining room, bar, sauna, outdoor whirlpool, large fishing and swimming pond, games room, exercise machines, and shop. Massage therapist in residence.

Bugaboo Lodge

Jocelyn Lang

Located 170 kilometres (105 miles) southwest of Banff via Radium, B.C. The heliport is near the town of Spillimacheen, B.C.

Three- and six-night packages: $1,122–2,121 per person. Children's rates available.

Bugaboo Lodge has double rooms with private bathrooms. Other facilities include living room with fireplace, dining room, bar, sauna, whirlpool, games room, tennis courts, fishing and swimming pond, and shop. Massage therapist in residence.

Bobbie Burns Lodge

Rob Rohn

*Located 170 kilometres (105 miles) southwest
of Banff via Golden, B.C. The heliport is
near the town of Parson, B.C.*

Three- and six-night packages: $1,122–2,121
per person. Children's rates available.

Bobbie Burns Lodge has double rooms with
private bathrooms. Other facilities include living
room with fireplace, dining room, bar, sauna,
whirlpool, games room, fishing and swimming pond, and shop. Massage therapist in
residence.

Blue Mountain Lodge

Hugh and Irene Simpson
Mail: Box 2763
Banff, AB   T0L 0C0
(403) 762-5134

*Located one block from Banff Avenue, corner
of Caribou and Muskrat Streets.*

Ten rooms and two cabins: One or two
people $50–70 with shared bathroom, $70–80
with private bathroom; add'l person $10.
Daily and weekly winter rates available.

A turn-of-the-century inn with period décor and mountain views. Guests help themselves
to a full Continental breakfast. There are guest kitchen facilities, a guest lounge, complimentary tea and coffee, cable TV, and sun decks with barbecues. The inn, a central
Banff landmark, is minutes from shopping and restaurants and within easy walking distance of hiking trails. Pets in residence. No smoking. Visa accepted.

Rocky Mountain Bed and Breakfast

223 Otter Street
Mail: Box 2528
Banff, AB   T0L 0C0
(403) 762-4811

Corner of Wolf and Otter streets.

Six rooms: One person $35–75, two people $40–80.
Five rooms with cooking facilities: One person $50–80, two people $55–85.

A former C.P.R. boarding house from the 1920s, with period décor in the common areas and the upper-story rooms. The lower story has been renovated in bright country style, with wainscoting. A sitting room with fireplace on the lower story and a sitting area on the upper story are for the exclusive use of guests. Rooms with cooking facilities have private bathrooms; other rooms share bathrooms. A hot breakfast is served daily, summer and winter. Bikes can be rented in the summer. The hosts are happy to recommend highlights of the area's national parks, Banff, Jasper, Yoho, and Glacier. No smoking. No pets. Recently given a one-star rating by the Alberta Accommodation Grading Program.

Luna Lodge

Joyce Luna
160 Rundle Crescent
Mail: Box 1136
Canmore, AB   T0L 0M0
(403) 678-4849

Take the Canmore exit from Highway 1;
follow the signs to the Nordic Centre.
Continue across the Bow River, and take a
sharp right turn as you come off the bridge.

Two units: One person $45, two people $55–60, add'l person $10.

A log house with a verandah and upper deck overlooking the Bow River and providing a panorama of mountains. The house was built in 1913 as the directors' cabin for visiting executives at the Canadian Anthracite Coal Company. Inside are period furniture, a large guest living room with fireplace and grand piano, and contemporary art work. Each guest room retains its original adjacent bathroom with only small changes for modern convenience. Guests fish for trout; a boat launch is a few steps away. Nordic skiing is popular in winter. Reservations with deposit recommended. Cash and traveller's cheques only. Dog in residence. Children over six welcome. No smoking.

The Georgetown Inn

Doreen and Barry Jones and family
1101 Bow Valley Trail
Mail: Box 3151
Canmore, AB   T0L 0M0
(403) 678-3439

From Highway 1, take the Canmore exit onto Highway 1A. Very close to the hospital.

Fourteen rooms: Low season, one person $65, two people $75; high season, one person $75, two people $85; add'l person $20.

An inn at the gateway to Banff National Park, 20 minutes' drive from the town of Banff. Full English breakfast and afternoon tea with homemade scones and jam are bed-and-breakfast features the hosts have brought with them from Britain. Guest rooms have mountain views, antique furniture, ensuite bathrooms, and single or queen-sized beds with down duvets. One room has been designed for people with disabilities. The inn has a full-service dining room and a traditional British-style pub, the Miner's Lamp, both with fireplaces. Nearby are hiking, golfing, horseback riding, fishing, canoeing, kayaking, whitewater rafting, mountaineering, parapenting, and, in winter, skating, Nordic and downhill skiing, and ice climbing. The inn is minutes from Canmore, site of the Nordic ski events at the 1988 Olympics, and one hour from the Lake Louise, Norquay, Sunshine, and Nakiska downhill ski areas. Wheelchair accessible. Children welcome. Smoking restricted to the pub and outdoor patios.

Jasper Park Lodge

Mail: Box 40
Jasper, AB T0E 1E0
(403) 852-3301   Fax: (403) 852-5107
Toll-free: 800-441-1414

Five kilometres (3 miles) east of the town of Jasper.

Four hundred forty-two rooms and suites: One or two people $87–212
in winter, $137–329 in spring/fall, $259–444 in summer.

A full-facility resort with a lodge and log cabins on immaculate grounds, on nine hundred acres on the shore of a lake in Jasper National Park, five kilometres from the town of Jasper. Elks, bighorn sheep, deer, and Canada geese are often seen at the resort. The lodge's main restaurant is one of four in Alberta to have received the American Automobile Association's four-diamond award for fine cuisine. In the lodge are boutiques, licensed lounges, and a nightclub. The lodge's conference facilities received a 1992 Pinnacle award from *Successful Meetings* magazine, an award presented to the best meeting and convention hotels worldwide. Outside are a heated pool, tennis courts, an 18-hole championship golf course, a full-service health club, and a four-kilometre lakeshore path. The golf course has been voted the number one golf resort in Canada by *Golf Magazine* and has twice in the past four years received the Golf Tee award from *Meetings and Conventions* magazine. Horseback riding, boating, canoeing, cycling, and hiking are popular. In the winter, skating and downhill and cross-country skiing are close by, and canyon crawling, heli-skiing, and guided snowmobile tours are available by arrangement. The downhill ski hill offers 2,300 vertical feet on one thousand acres.

Marmot Lodge

Connaught Drive
Mail: Box 687
Jasper, AB   T0E 1E0
(403) 852-4471
Toll-free from western Canada:
800-661-6521
Fax: (403) 852-3280

Located on the main street in Jasper.

One hundred six rooms: Call for rates.
Midweek rates available.
Three-day skiing packages available.

A lodge with décor that reflects the four major historical influences on western Canada: the Plains Indians, the Hudson's Bay Company, the railway, and the R.C.M.P. Well-maintained landscaping complements the cedar buildings. There are family suites, double and single rooms, newly renovated kitchen suites, and six rooms designed for the convenience of guests with disabilities. Forty-eight of the rooms are air-conditioned, and some feature river rock fireplaces. The lodge has a restaurant and licensed lounge, an indoor pool, a sauna, a whirlpool, and a nature trail suitable for people with limited mobility.

Astoria Hotel

404 Connaught Drive
Mail: Box 1710
Jasper, AB   T0E 1E0
(403) 852-3351
Toll-free: 800-661-7343
Fax: (403) 852-5472

Located in the centre of town on the main street, one block from the VIA Rail station and the bus station.

Thirty-five rooms: $81–108 in summer, $53–70 in winter, $43–54 in fall. Off-season rates available.
Skiing packages available.

A small hotel that includes complimentary passes to Jasper's Aquatic and Activity Centre in its regular room rates. The centre, three blocks away, has a lap pool, a wading pool, a water slide, a sauna, a whirlpool, a steambath, racquet courts, a weight room, a skating rink, a curling rink, a climbing wall, and outdoor tennis courts. Each of the rooms in the hotel has cable TV, a small fridge, a telephone, and a private bathroom. The hotel has a restaurant, Papa George's, that serves Continental cuisine and a bar with a country pub atmosphere. The hotel is a short bus ride away from powder snow in the Rockies. In summer, there are daily pick-ups for sightseeing tours in Jasper National Park.

Tyax Mountain Lake Resort

Tyaughton Lake Road
Gold Bridge, BC   V0K 1P0
(604) 238-2221
Fax: (604) 238-2528

Located 200 kilometres (125 miles) north of Vancouver, close to Gold Bridge. Accessible by car, train, snowbus, and floatplane.

Twenty-nine rooms: In summer, one person $90, two people $98. In winter, one person $80, two people $88.
Four chalets: In summer $200 for four people, in winter $180 for four people, add'l person $20.
Tent sites: $18 for two people, add'l person $8.

A resort on the shores of Tyaughton Lake in the remote Chilcotin mountains, 125 miles north of Vancouver. A large lodge built of huge golden spruce logs has a 30-foot-high fireplace, a restaurant, a Western-style bar, a conference room, a fitness centre, a sauna, and a games room. Outdoor amenities include a whirlpool, a tennis court, and a children's playground. Each chalet has three or four bedrooms, is self-contained, and has its own beach. Rainbow trout and Dolly Varden fishing. The resort organizes horseback riding, guided gold panning, fly-out fishing, trapshooting, and archery. Canoes, rowboats, paddle boats, sailboats, and motorboats are provided. Hiking among alpine meadows, glacier-fed creeks and lakes, and forests. In winter, guests heli-ski, cross-country ski, ride snowmobiles and sleighs, skate, and ice fish.

Big Bar Guest Ranch

Brian Gunn
Mail: Box 27
Clinton, BC   V0K 1K0
(604) 459-2333
Fax: (604) 459-2333

Fifty-six kilometres (35 miles) north of Clinton (Highway 97). Transport from B.C. Rail station or Greyhound bus depot at Clinton can be arranged in advance.

Twelve rooms: One person $80, two people 140, child 8–14 $40, child 3–7 $25, children under 3 free.
Two cabins: Two people $75, add'l adult $12, child 3–7 $5.
RV sites: $10 per person and $10 per vehicle per day.
Discounts for longer stays and groups. Various packages offered.

A ranch on 104 acres of rolling pasture and pine forests in the valley between the Marble Mountains and Big Bar Mountain. The ranch offers riding instruction at all levels of experience and short, all-day, and four-day camp-out riding trips. Children are catered to. Rooms in a new guest house have private bathrooms. Six of the rooms have bunk lofts for children. Rates for the rooms include three meals a day in a family-style licensed dining room. Evening barbecues in summer. Log cabins overlook a lake. Each cabin has one bedroom and a loft, a kitchen, a bathroom, and a wood stove. A restored pioneer log building that was once part of the OK Cattle Ranch has a fireside lounge, a billiards room, and a covered verandah for watching sunsets. The ranch offers an outdoor hot tub, a video room, a telescope for star gazing, and casual entertainment including campfire sing-alongs and slide shows. Guests canoe, swim, fish, hike, and pan for gold on the Fraser River. Winter activities include cross-country skiing, skating, and sleigh rides. Deposit of $100 required to hold reservation. No smoking in dining room or guest rooms. Pets welcome.

Kelly Lake Ranch Bed and Breakfast

Karin Lange
Kelly Lake Road
Mail: Box 547
Clinton, BC   V0K 1K0
(604) 459-2313

Located 17 kilometres (11 miles) west of Clinton on paved road.

Three log cabins and ranch house rooms: One person $30–40, two
people $40–50, add'l person $10.
Ten tent sites: $7, hot shower $3.
Four RV sites: $12.
Accommodation for 8–10 horses: $10 per horse per day, including hay.

A B&B with a ranch house and three log cabins, on the Cariboo Gold Rush Trail. During
the gold rush, the road passed between the barn and the present-day ranch house of this
240-acre ranch. Today, B.C. Rail has a flag stop on the ranch. Guests have breakfast
in a glassed-in sunroom overlooking gardens and corrals; the cabins have kitchens where
guests prepare their other meals. For horse owners, a bale-and-breakfast special includes
access to hundreds of miles of open riding trails. Children feed the goats, sheep, rabbits,
peacocks, and chickens. Cross-country skiing, fishing (or ice fishing), and biking are popular. Trail riding is available at nearby dude ranches, and weekend painting workshops
are held on site.

Circle H Mountain Lodge

Mitch and Daphne Henselwood
Jesmond
Mail: Box 7
Clinton, BC   V0K 1K0
(604) 459-2565
October to May mailing address:
3086 Babich Street
Abbotsford, BC   V2S 2H7
(604) 850-1873   Fax: (604) 850-1873

Turn west at the Esso station in Clinton and
travel 16 kilometres (10 miles). Just before Downing Provincial Park, turn right and fol-
low the dirt road for 24 kilometres (15 miles). Pick-up in Clinton can be arranged.

Five lodge rooms, four sleeping cabins: One person $89, child 6–12 $69. Rates include meals and riding. Weekly rates and group discounts available. Open May to October.

A horse ranch high on the rolling Cariboo plateau. A lodge and log cabins accommodate 18 guests. There are two guest bathrooms and a shower room in the lodge. Meals are cooked in a wood stove—the focal point of the dining area—and there is an unlicensed log-cabin lounge with a fridge available for guests' beverages. There are trail rides twice a day and all-day rides into upland ranges twice a week. Hiking through alpine meadows, fishing, and canoeing are popular. The lodge has an outdoor pool and a sauna. In winter, there are 75 kilometres of maintained trails for cross-country skiing and a pond to skate on. Families welcome. Babysitting can be arranged.

Loon Lake Resort

Tom and Elaine Burgess
17 Mile Loon Lake Road
Mail: RR 1, Cache Creek, BC   V0K 1H0
(604) 459-2537   Fax: (604) 459-2022

From Cache Creek, drive north on Highway
97 to 20 Mile House. Turn right on Loon
Lake Road and continue 27 kilometres (17
miles). All paved.

Thirteen bring-your-own-bedding cabins: One or two people $24–45, add'l person $3–5.
Twenty-four campsites: One or two people $12, add'l person $2, children under six free.

A resort on 29 acres of scenic Cariboo waterfront. Housekeeping cabins have refrigerators, stoves, dishes, and running water. Nine of the cabins have private bathrooms. Campsites have water and power. A large grassy area is a playing field for children. On site are a restaurant and lounge, laundry facilities, a central building with hot showers and flush toilets, and a small store selling groceries, fishing licences, bait, and ice. The resort has boats for rent. Hiking, horseback riding, swimming, fishing, ice fishing, cross-country skiing, and sledding are popular.

Eagan Lake Ranch Resort

Eric and Ronnie Cleveland and family
Eagan Lake Road
Mail: Box 34
Bridge Lake, BC V0K 1E0
(604) 593-4343

Seventeen kilometres (11 miles) south of Bridge Lake, which is on
Highway 24. Approximately halfway between 93 Mile House on
Highway 97 and Little Fort on Highway 5. Pick-up service at 70 or 100
Mile House by request (extra charge).

Seven cabins: Two people $25–50, add'l person $4, child 4–11 $1.50,
children under 4 free. Pet $1. Discount on reservations of one week or
more. Winter rates November to April. Bedding and utensils supplied
by arrangement at extra charge.

A guest ranch on the shore of Eagan Lake in the heart of the Cariboo. Family-sized, rustic log cabins have wood stoves and refrigerators. Meals are not provided. A central shower
building with flush toilets and laundromat is open in season (outhouses only, off-season).
Guests fish for kokanee and rainbow trout, take guided trail rides in small groups, hike,
swim, boat, and help with ranch activities. In winter, ice fishing and cross-country skiing
are popular. Pets welcome. Pay phone, camping, and RV parking. Early reservations
recommended.

Minac Lodge on Canim Lake

Mail: Eagle Creek, BC   V0K 1L0
(604) 397-2416

Take Highway 97 to Canim Lake turnoff and turn right to Forest Grove Esso. Follow Canim-Hendrix Road to Eagle Creek.

Nine lodge rooms: One person $32.50, two people $50.75.
Two cabins: Small cabin (sleeps two) $45, large log cabin (sleeps four) $60.
Eight-room bunkhouse: $20 per room.

A lakeside lodge with lodge rooms, two cabins, and an eight-room bunkhouse. The lodge, built of log slab in 1948, is a local landmark that stands where Eagle Creek flows into Canim Lake. The bunkhouse has central washrooms and sleeps two people per room. Rates for both lodge and bunkhouse rooms include breakfast. The cabins have kitchens. A licensed, air-conditioned dining room in the lodge serves lunch and dinner at reasonable prices. The lodge has a library with fireplace and a cocktail area. A swimming beach is nearby, and motorboats, canoes, pedal boats, and fishing tackle are available for use on the lake. Guests visit Canim Falls and hike or cross-country ski. The lodge has a children's playground, a video machine, and a games room. Not suitable for pets. Pick-up available.

108 Resort

Mail: C–2
108 Mile Ranch, BC   V0K 2Z0
(604) 791-5211
Toll-free: 800-667-5233
Fax: (604) 791-6537

Thirteen kilometres (8 miles) north of 100 Mile House, turn west off
Highway 97 and follow the signposts to the resort.

Sixty-two rooms: High season (June 1 to September 30, December 21 to
January 3), one person $105–172, two people $115–172, add'l adult
$10, children under 12 free. Low season, one person $90–152, two
people $100–152, add'l adult $10, children under 12 free. Golf and
horseback riding packages available.

A resort on 600 acres beside the Cariboo's Gold Rush Trail. On-site amenities include
a championship golf course with pro shop, power carts, and a driving range; stables with
horses for every level of experience; four tennis courts; a volleyball court; and trails for
hiking, mountain biking, and cross-country skiing. Wagon rides and canoe rentals are
available; sleigh rides in winter. A whirlpool, sauna, and heated pool (seasonal) are popular. Accommodation choices range from standard rooms, each with two double beds,
through housekeeping rooms, each with small fridge, stove, and sitting area, to large suites
for six, each with kitchen. All rooms have views of the golf course, lakes, and wood-
lands. A full-service restaurant has a sunset view and an award-winning wine list. There
are also a licensed lounge, a gift shop, and full conference facilities. Pets allowed. Smoking in some rooms.

Ten-ee-ah Lodge

Peter and Ulli Vogler
Mail: Box 157
Lac La Hache, BC   V0K 1T0
(604) 395-7100
Radio phone: N692024 on JS channel, 100 Mile House.

From Highway 97, turn east at Lac La Hache and follow the signs for
28 kilometres (17 miles) to the lodge.

Nine cabins: Two people $85, add'l person $15, children under 12 30%
discount, children under 3 free.
Tent sites, with use of central shower building: Two people $12, add'l
person $3.

A lodge that is the only property on Spout Lake, enjoying a six-mile-long private
playground, where guests swim, fish, canoe, and, in winter, dog-sled. Modern one-, two-,
and three-bedroom cabins have panoramic views across the lake to the forested slopes
of Mount Timothy. All cabins have living rooms, dining areas, kitchens, and bathrooms.
The lodge has a lounge with stone fireplace, a bar, a games room, a huge deck, and a
licensed restaurant where Swiss pastries and homemade bread and ice cream are specialties. Horses are hired by the hour or for two- to five-day guided trail rides. Fishing trips
to a wilderness lake accessible only by float plane are popular. In winter, there are groomed
cross-country ski trails and miles of snowshoeing trails. Pick-up is available (at extra charge)
from Lac La Hache, Williams Lake, and 100 Mile House.

Timothy Lake Resort

Mail: Box 42
Lac La Hache, BC   V0K 1T0
(604) 396-7367

Nineteen kilometres (12 miles) east of Lac La Hache. The road is paved part of the way and is good gravel the rest of the way.

Five cabins: One or two people $35, add'l person $4, children free.
Seven RV sites: $10. Tent sites: $8 per tent.
Open May to October.

A quiet lakeside resort surrounded by trees. The lake is good for swimming and is stocked with rainbow trout every year. Each lakefront cabin—two duplex units and one single unit—has a separate bedroom with double bed, a bathroom with tub or shower, and a fire pit out front. Wood is provided free. Linen is supplied by arrangement. The resort has a shower building, laundry facilities, a playground, a sandy beach, and beach toys. The resort is suitable for family reunions. Crib and highchair available. Boats, motors, canoes, and paddle boats are available for rent. A small on-site store has fishing licences and tackle as well as basic necessities. Pets allowed.

Fir Crest Resort

Jim and Virginia Wilson
Fir Crest Road
Mail: RR 1   C–9
Lac La Hache, BC   V0K 1T0
(604) 396-7337

Two minutes from Highway 97, 6 kilometres (4 miles) north of the town of Lac La Hache.

Twelve cabins: One bedroom, two people $33 ($198 per week); two bedrooms, four people $39 ($234 per week); add'l person $3; cot or crib $3.
RV sites: $13.50. Tent sites: $10.

A resort that has self-contained cabins on a lake, with a quarter mile of gently sloping sandy beach outside their front doors. The cabins have kitchens, indoor plumbing, and linen. Lac La Hache is pleasantly warm for summer swimming and is well known for its kokanee and lake char. The resort's marina provides docking facilites for guests' boats and has canoes, rowboats, and motorboats for rent. Tackle and fishing licences are available at an on-site convenience store. A large games room offers pool, ping-pong, coin games, and TV. There are also outdoor games, including horseshoes and volleyball, and a children's playground. Pets welcome.

Eagle's Nest Resort

Petrus and Enubi Rykes
Mail: Box 3403
Anahim Lake, BC   V0L 1C0
(604) 742-3707
Radio telephone: Eagle's Nest N 690300, Nimpo Lake JR Channel
(ask for Prince George radio operator).

Eight kilometres (5 miles) west of Anahim Lake on Highway 20.
Wilderness Airlines has daily flights between Vancouver and Anahim
Lake.

Three cabins, one tepee: One person $30–35, two people $35–40,
family $40–45.

A secluded resort surrounded by three mountain ranges in the Chilcotin, with a lodge on
the tip of a private peninsula and cabins and a sleeping-only tepee stretched along the
lakeshore. The rustic log cabins have wood stoves, propane lighting, and outdoor plumbing, with various combinations of single, double, and bunk beds. The lodge has bathroom
and laundry facilities, a large sitting area with fireplace, a hot tub under the pines, a gift
shop, and a smoke house. Guests dine at the lodge by arrangement—vegetarian and European cuisines are specialties. Boats, motors, and canoes can be rented for fly-fishing. Guests
hike in Tweedsmuir Provincial Park and skate and cross-country ski in winter.

Elkin Creek Guest Ranch

Nemaiah Valley, BC
Mail: 4462 Marion Road
North Vancouver, BC   V7K 2V2
(604) 984-4666
Fax: (604) 984-4686

Seven hundred kilometres (430 miles) from Vancouver. Follow Highway 1 east to Cache Creek. Turn north on Highway 97 to Williams Lake. Take Highway 20 to Hanceville. At Hanceville, turn left (pavement ends shortly after this turn) and follow the signs to Nemaiah Valley. Pick-up can be arranged from Williams Lake. Airstrip on the ranch.

Seven cabins: From $135 per person per day, third person in cabin $70, children under 12 half rate. Rates include meals and activities.

A working ranch in one of the wildest, most rugged, and most unspoiled areas left in North America. The ranch's hay fields, horses, and grazing cattle are in a valley alongside Vedan Lake. The view of the surrounding Coast Mountains is dominated by Mount Tatlow, which rises 10,000 feet above the valley floor. Each modern, traditionally built log cabin has two bedrooms, two ensuite bathrooms with showers, a living room, and a verandah with view. Choice of two single beds or one double bed in the bedrooms. The ranch has a dining room, a lounge/Western bar with a large rock fireplace, a reading room, a games room, and a barbecue pit. Activities include watching ranchers at work, trail rides for one day and several days, windsurfing, sailing, water-skiing, fishing, exploring the lakes by canoe, archery, trapshooting, panning for gold, hiking, and going on photo-safaris in a four-wheel-drive jeep.

Bowron Lake Lodge and Resorts

Mail: 672 Walkem Street
Quesnel, BC   V2J 2J7
(604) 992-2733

On Bowron Lake, 25 minutes from Wells.

Twenty cabins: One person $40, two people $50–70, add'l person $5.

A lodge at the entrance to Bowron Lake Provincial Park, with 2,200 feet of beach on Bowron Lake and two miles of private river frontage where sockeye salmon spawn. Canoe trips on the Bowron Lake chain are popular with wilderness enthusiasts. Wildlife and water-fowl are abundant. Light-weight canoes and boats are rented at the lodge. Other activities include hiking on three miles of private trails, visiting alpine meadows, and seeing the historic town of Barkerville, half an hour away. Guests stay in modern one-, two-, and three-room cabins and in a big house that accommodates eight (or more) for $100. Dining facilities with home-cooked meals in the lodge. Lakeshore and riverfront sites for campers, with hot showers and flush toilets.

Mount Layton Hot Springs Resort

Mail: Box 550
Terrace, BC V8G 4B5
(604) 798-2214
Fax: (604) 798-2478

On Highway 37 South, a 15-minute drive
from Terrace.

Twenty-two rooms: One person $60, two
people $66, add'l person $6.

A resort at a natural mineral hot springs, with
water slides, a giant pool, and a separate
therapeutic pool. Children play on a turtle slide and "UFO H_2O," a water attraction
originally at Vancouver's Expo '86. The resort has a dining room, restaurant, and lounge.
A roof-top beer garden with mountain views is open during the summer months. Lakelse
Lake is half a mile away. The area offers fresh and saltwater fishing. Professional guiding
is available at the resort.

Campbell's Babine Lodge

Don and Karren Campbell
Mail: Box 9 SS 1
Topley Landing, BC V0J 1W0
(604) 697-2310

From Burns Lake, follow Highway 16 west to
Granisle turnoff. Take Highway 108 north to
Topley Landing. Paved roads to the gate.

Six cabins: Two people $40, add'l person
$5. Weekly and monthly rates available.
Twenty-eight RV sites: $14.

A lodge with six cabins on Babine Lake, British Columbia's longest natural lake. The
cabins have hot water and flush toilets. Two of the cabins have housekeeping facilities.
Breakfast provided on request. A licensed dining room, a laundromat, and shower facilities are in the lodge. Guests swim, hunt, rent or charter boats, and fish for rainbow, cut-
throat, steelhead, and salmon in Babine Lake and surrounding lakes and rivers. The resort
has a new cement boat launch and docking facilities and sells auto and marine gas and
propane.

Driftwood Lodge

Jean and Norm Isaac, Alison and Keith Douglas
Babine Lake Road
Mail: RR 2   Site 53   C–11
Smithers, BC   V0J 2N0
(604) 847-5016

Twelve kilometres (7 miles) from Smithers.

Five rooms: One person $55, two people $90. Rates include breakfast.
Open year-round by reservation.

A lodge on 114 acres above the Bulkley Valley. The lodge is a 7,000-square-foot log building with five bedrooms, each with double bed and ensuite bathroom. A 1,500-square-foot "great room," for gathering and dining, has a vaulted ceiling and a stone fireplace. Evening meals are available on weekends. Downstairs are a recreation room and a hot tub with a view of the mountains. Alpine hiking, trail riding, golfing, fishing, skiing, and snowmobiling are popular activities in the area. Adult oriented. No smoking. No pets. Visa and MasterCard accepted.

Tukii Lodge

Marilyn and David Hooper
Mail: Box 3693 T
Smithers, BC V0J 2N0
(604) 847-8122

On Babine Lake at Smithers Landing, 72 kilometres (45 miles) north of Smithers.

Six cabins (each sleeps 3–5 people): $65–90 per night.
Two wilderness camps (each sleeps 7–12 people): $140 per night.

A lodge with cabins and wilderness camps on Babine Lake, which is 110 miles long and has 380 miles of shoreline. Modern housekeeping cabins are well spaced among the trees and have views of the lake. There is a licensed dining room in the lodge. Fly, spinner, and troll fishing on Babine Lake and on the small, remote lakes and streams nearby. Ice fishing, snowmobiling, and cross-country skiing in winter. Amenities include boat rentals, charter boat trips, fishing guide service, fish-smoking facilities, barbecue pits, and a store with groceries, tackle, and gear.

Beaver Point Resort on Tchesinkut Lake

Jake and Brenda Hiebert
Mail: Box 587
Burns Lake, BC   V0J 1E0
(604) 695-6519
(604) 698-7665 (off season)

Located 16 kilometres (10 miles) south of Burns Lake on Highway 35.

Four cabins (each sleeps up to four people): One person $20, two people $27, four people $30.
One cabin (sleeps up to six people): $50.
Fifty tent and RV sites: $8 per tent, $10–12 per RV.
Open May 15 to September 15.

Self-contained one-room log cabins, tent sites, and RV sites, set among trees and over-looking a lake. Each cabin has two double beds or bunks; guests bring their own bedding. Electric lights and fridge, propane cooking and heating. There is a water tap outside each cabin. Grassy campsites are close to the lakeshore. Campers have the use of picnic tables, fire rings, and coin-operated showers. Outdoor toilets. An on-site store offers fast food, basic groceries, local crafts, and fishing tackle. The lake is known for its sport fishing. Guests rent boats and motors or use the resort's launching and docking facilities for their own boats. Canoes and water bikes are available for rent.

Birch Bay Resort

Mail: Box 484
Fraser Lake, BC   V0J 1S0
(604) 699-8484

From Highway 16, 1 kilometre (1 mile) west of Fraser Lake, turn south onto François Lake Road and travel 30 kilometres (19 miles) to the resort, on François Lake.

Six cabins: Two people $20–40, add'1 person $2. Bedding charge of $2 per bed.
Ten RV sites: Two people $12, add'1 person $1.
Ten tent sites: Two people $10, add'1 person $1.

A lakeside resort with self-contained cabins, a campground, and RV sites. The self-contained cabins are right on the beach, where children swim and fishing enthusiasts pull up their boats. Launching and marina facilities; boats available for rent. A small store at the resort sells basic groceries, fishing licences, and gear. Guests pitch horseshoes while children play in a small playground. A network of hiking trails leads up into the surrounding hills. Challenging golf course within 10 kilometres. Reservations recommended.

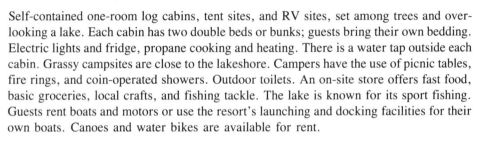

Nechako Lodge

Josef and Elisabeth Doerig
Kenney Dam, Knewstubb Lake
Mail: Box 2413
Vanderhoof, BC V0J 3A0
(604) 690-7740
Fax: (604) 690-7740

In Vanderhoof, turn south off Highway 16 at Nechako Road. Follow signs—"Resort Lakes," "Knewstubb Lake"—for 90 kilometres (56 miles).

Six rooms: One person $43–50, add'l person $9.
Four cabins: One or two people $47–50, add'l person $8.
Guided outdoor activities package available.

A secluded lakeside resort at the east end of the Nechako Reservoir, which offers hundreds of miles of boating and fishing. The historic MacKenzie Trail and the spectacular mountains and glaciers of Tweedsmuir Provincial Park are within easy reach. Guests stay in the lodge with American plan or rent one of the self-contained log cabins. The lodge offers a short-order menu all day and a Swiss or Canadian set evening meal. There is a licensed lounge with a fireplace. A package with American plan includes guided fishing, hiking, canoeing, horseback riding, boat tours, fly-ins, and pick-up from Prince George. Nechako Lodge is popular for working retreats, meetings, and seminars. Reservations recommended.

Hidden Lake Lodge

Paul Brenneisen
Hidden Lake Road
Mail: General Delivery
Dunster, BC V0J 1J0
(604) 968-4327
Fax: (604) 968-4327

Twenty kilometres (12 miles) east of McBride; 50 kilometres (31 miles) west of Mount Robson Park.

Four cabins: Two people $50–70, four people $90. Open approximately May to October.

A wilderness lodge and cabins in the Robson Valley between the Rocky and Cariboo mountains. Furnished cabins provide a base for exploring Mount Robson Park. Guests do their own cooking or have their meals at the lodge. Activity programs are offered. A canoe is available. Bears, moose, beavers, blue herons, and waterfowl are seen on the grounds. Nearby are Hidden Lake and an interpretive trail.

Queen Charlotte Lodge

Naden Harbour
Queen Charlotte Islands
Mail: 7069 Winston Street
Burnaby, BC   V5A 3R1
(604) 420-7197
Toll-free from Canada: 800-665-9980
Toll-free from U.S.: 800-688-8959
Fax: (604) 420-9194

Naden Harbour is on the northeastern side of Graham Island in the
Queen Charlotte Islands.

Fishing packages: Four days/three nights $2,275, five days/four nights
$2,475, one week $4,400. Open May to September.

A Queen Charlotte Island fishing lodge on a forested shoreline, built on the site of an old whaling station. Lodgepole pine construction blends with the surroundings and creates a homestead atmosphere inside. Twenty-four spacious guest rooms have twin or queen-sized beds, ensuite bathrooms, and harbour views. A central licensed lounge/sitting area has a 36-foot-high fireplace built of local stone. A hand-crafted curved staircase leads to a mezzanine dining room where full-course and buffet meals are served. Complimentary wine with dinner. Haida art and jewellery, books on Northwest Coast art, and custom-designed clothing are for sale in a gift shop. There are a hot tub, a sauna, and a games area with snooker and games tables. Rates include return airfare from Vancouver, meals, boats, tackle, bait, all-weather flotation gear, escort duty by the M.V. *Driftwood* (with modern facilities), and care of guests' catch. Professional guiding can be arranged. The Queen Charlotte Islands are known for chinook, coho salmon, and halibut fishing. Other activities include hiking, kayaking, photography, and exploring ancient forests. Wildlife is abundant.

Stikine Riversong

Dan Pakula and David Fisher
Mail: General Delivery
Telegraph Creek, BC   V0J 2W0
(604) 235-3196

*Located in the "old town" of Telegraph Creek on the bank of the
Stikine River.*

Eight rooms: One person $42, two people $46–52, add'l person $9. Use
of kitchen facilities $7.50.

Accommodation in Telegraph Creek, which was historically the head of navigation of the
640-kilometre-long Stikine River and is the only town along its banks. In the town, many
of the original buildings from the gold rush of the late 19th century still stand, including
a Hudson's Bay Company store that was built in 1897 at Hudson's Bay Flat and moved
to its present site in 1903. Five of Stikine Riversong's rooms are in the old store and three
in a renovated Hudson's Bay warehouse. The rooms are large, and kitchen facilities are
available. A riverside café offers home-style cooking including fresh Stikine salmon and
homemade bread, soups, and desserts. The area is known for its abundant and varied wildlife
and the unique geological formations of the Lower Stikine River Recreation Area and Mount
Edziza Provincial Park—the Grand Canyon of the Stikine. There are riverboat charters
for day trips and longer excursions to Wrangell and Petersburg, Alaska. Guided hikes
into the Grand Canyon are also available.

Southwind Wilderness Retreat

Mail: Box 80   Department SP
Carcross, YT   Y0B 1B0
Radio phone: 2M-3285, Carcross Channel
(monitored 1:00-2:00 p.m. and
8:00-9:00 p.m.)

Accessible by air and water only.

Log cabin or tepee: Six days $1,320 per
person.
Open March and April and from June to
September.

A wilderness camp on a large interlake waterway at the headwaters of the Yukon River.
Guests enjoy views of mountains and lakes from canoes and motorboats while fishing for
grayling and trout. The resort arranges day-long excursions. Guests in search of greater
challenges go on overnight climbing adventures (class 1 through class 5) and, in spring,
cross-country skiing expeditions with dogsled or snowmobile support. Marksmanship
instruction at an on-site shooting range is available on request. Home-cooked meals and
privacy are specialties. Return charter flight from Whitehorse included in the rate.

Barney's Fishing and Tours

Mail: General Delivery
Tagish, YT   Y0B 1T0
(403) 399-3474

Located southeast of Whitehorse, the Tagish
Lake system is reached via Highway 8, which
runs between the Alaska Highway (1) and the
Klondike Highway (2).

One cabin (sleeps six): Call for rates.
Fishing and sightseeing charters: Call for
rates.
RV and tent sites: Included in charter rates.

A log cabin in a northern wilderness mountain setting on the Tagish Lake system, accessible by water only. Drop-off and pick-up service is provided. The cabin has propane light
and wood heat. Guests supply their own food, bedding, and fishing gear. A small boat
is available for use at the cabin. The lakes abound with fish—lake trout, northern pike,
arctic grayling, lingcod, and whitefish. A 14-foot boat with motor is available for rent.
Guided charters are available on an 18½-foot Sangster Craft. The boat's captain was born
in the Yukon and has fished the Tagish area for over 25 years.

The Cabin Bed and Breakfast

Mail: Box 5334
Haines Junction, YT   Y0B 1L0
(403) 634-2626

Located near Kathleen Lake in southwestern Yukon at kilometre 219
(mile 136) on Haines Road, 27 kilometres (17 miles) from Haines
Junction.

Four cabins: One person $35, two people $50, add'l person $15, child
under 13 $10.
Rates include Continental breakfast.

Semi-serviced light housekeeping cabins on a large acreage with a view of King's Throne
Mountain. Nearby Kluane National Park has the highest mountains in Canada and the
largest non-polar icefield in the world and is known for its abundant plants and wildlife.
Activities include flightseeing over the icefield ranges, white-water rafting on the Tat-
shenshini River, horseback riding, mountain biking, hiking, fishing, canoeing, and visiting nearby Kathleen Lake. There are picnic tables, a campfire circle, and an outdoor sauna
and shower. Pets welcome. Smoking and non-smoking cabins.

Hakai Beach Resort

Hakai Recreational Park
Mail: 580 Hornby Street, Suite 440
Vancouver, BC   V6C 3B6
(604) 689-9313
Toll-free: 800-668-FISH(3474)
Fax: (604) 689-9312

Located four hundred kilometres (250 miles) north of Vancouver on the northern end of Calvert Island. Fly from Vancouver airport to Port Hardy, then by float plane to the resort.

Twelve suites: Four or five days $1,995 per person.

A 214-acre oceanfront fly-in fishing resort in Hakai Recreational Park, 400 kilometres (250 miles) north of Vancouver. Rates include meals, liquor, return airfare from Vancouver, dawn-to-dusk fishing in 17-foot Boston Whalers with professional guides, tackle, bait, fuel, rain gear, and cleaning, vacuum packaging, and freezing of the catch. Rooms, some with lofts, have ensuite bathrooms, private sun decks, and views. There is a sitting area with an ocean view, couches, and a big fireplace. The resort has 6,000 feet of white sand beaches, hot tubs, a games room, and a workout centre. Guests' own catch is served on request. For business guests, the resort has a meeting room, audio-visual equipment, and a business centre with telephone and fax machine. The ancient forests of Hakai Recreational Park are nearby. Deposit of $500 per person required to hold reservation; balance due 30 days before arrival.

A Selection of Books Published by Gordon Soules Book Publishers

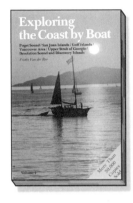

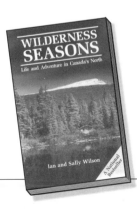